#  INSECTS
## *Their Secret World*

Six workers had the difficult task of holding the edges
of the leaves together. Page 204

EVELYN CHEESMAN

# INSECTS
## *Their Secret World*

*Illustrations by Arthur Smith*

**WILLIAM SLOANE ASSOCIATES**
*New York*

# Contents

# Contents

# Illustrations

# 1. The Elastic Body

IT IS A REMARKABLE FACT THAT THERE should be a greater variety of forms among the insects than in any other class of animal life. And it is another remarkable fact that this ability to vary is the cause of their successful exploitation of all this world's resources. However much of a nuisance insects may be, it must be admitted with grudging admiration—or ungrudging, if you happen to be an entomologist—that they can firmly establish themselves anywhere, even in what appear to be most unfavourable conditions. One can almost say that they are the real masters of the globe.

Looking deeper into the basis of this variability, one cannot fail to be struck by the advantages to such small beings as insects in possessing a peculiarly elastic type of bodily structure which lends itself to variation. In some groups this is more apparent than in others, some indeed seem to have come into existence endowed with a very large pack of cards, any of which may be turned uppermost if there should be any racial advantage to be enjoyed by doing so.

On every hand is a bewildering multitude of entirely different designs in the twenty-two orders under which insects are classified. Take a butterfly and a grasshopper and compare them—mode of development, type of body, habits, food—everything is different.

The butterfly passes through the egg stage, then a more or less prolonged grub or larval stage as a caterpillar, then through a resting stage and finally emerges as a mature insect. The wings are very large in proportion to the body, they are folded together flat when the insect is resting, flight is by beating the air. The mouth is a sucking proboscis through which fluid is imbibed. The legs are very slender and weak, fashioned for clinging.

Grasshoppers do not undergo a complete transformation. Whereas a caterpillar bears not the slightest resemblance to the parents, young hoppers even when just hatched from eggs are very like the parent form. There is no grub or a resting stage, each time the skin is shed the growth is advanced until after the fifth they become perfect insects. Wings are almost of the same length as the body, but are pleated fanwise and hidden inside a tough case when the insects are not flying. Flight is by an undulating movement. The mouth is not for drinking but consists of very strong jaws jagged at the tip for tearing and cutting up leaves. The forelegs are for climbing, with very useful spines to hold and balance; the hind pair are broad with extraordinarily powerful muscles for taking long leaps.

Here are two very well-known insects which can be compared any day, and their outward appearance is so different that it would be excusable to wonder how it is possible to put them both into the same class. Yet both are insects with the same type of physical system. This is why insects are such good colonists that they are to be found in any part of the world in any climate making use of all possible resources. No matter what disadvantages may be encountered, insects have a way of triumphing over everything to make a living—sometimes where nothing else could exist.

There are even tiny insects which have been discovered living inside quills of birds' feathers. They feed on the infinitesimal particles of debris collected from the walls of their very restricted dwelling. They go through their life history on this meagre diet and certainly are not worried by any rival claimants. There are minute parasitic insects which live on the tongues of horse flies.

In every order there are species which conform to a standard pattern with characters that are easily recognized, but in the same order the inherent variability is shown in forms that branch off from the main stem into extravagant over-development of some part of the body.

The grasshopper order goes in for long faces, but in the periscope grasshoppers this feature reaches its limit. They appear to be eating with their chests because the eyes are so far away from the mouth. They are very tiny insects peculiar to New Guinea and chiefly live in steamy forests, where they sit in heaps of dead leaves with the body hidden and the periscope sticking out. I have never seen them attacked by anything, but they probably have many enemies for they are alert to the slightest movement. Unless you approach very warily, a prodigious leap carries them among the bushes to be seen no more. The only way to catch them is with a rather large net brought down smartly from above, for they take off in any direction. This fantastic form serves them well. Racial pressure has been exercised and produced this result—a shuffling of the cards and a new design. Not a freak, but a successful little genus with its own place where it successfully propagates its kind.

There are freaks in the insect world which occasionally come to our notice. These are monstrosities which are very interesting as illustrations of the peculiar power to vary. It is clear that they occur very often but it is only by chance that we are lucky enough to find them. Some insects have produced a pair of perfect legs from a thigh, or two pairs of claws on one foot. A claw has even been known to develop from an eye. Even that sensitive organ the feeler or antenna has been known to develop from an insect's leg. There seems to be hardly any limit to what an insect can produce if some sort of physical disturbance has taken place during growth.

It is delightful to see what very simple characters are useful as tools and instruments. The human race accom-

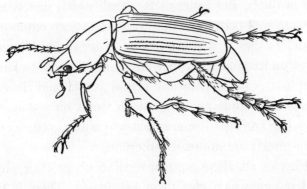

Monstrosities such as a pair of legs from a thigh or two pairs of claws prove disturbance during growth

plishes wonderful works, but needed the faculty of mind in order to invent tools and also hands with the very useful thumb to use the tools. Without these advantages insects carry out very intricate tasks with something that is grown on their own bodies. A spine here, a tuft of hair there—all have their special functions.

Rows of bristles in many designs make cleaning apparatus, a tuft of revolving soft hairs atomizes scent, a ring of stiff bristles on a bee's leg is a pollen basket, a stiff upper lip is a potter's trowel, a thick fringe of special hairs is an oar, a patch of velvet holds bubbles of air as an oxygen supply for insects swimming under water. And so on, and so on—the list might be prolonged almost interminably.

Their directive or mentorial powers—we must not call them mental powers—which guide all their actions are instincts. But some of the work which insects can do is so well performed that we have to keep reminding ourselves that it is subconscious. It seems as if insects must understand what they are doing, though we know that they cannot plan any action beforehand. It is a pleasure to study anything which works on a different principle and that is one reason why subjects connected with insects are unusually absorbing.

First of all, there are many points about their physical system which give them advantages. There is the body fluid, which is the blood. That is not isolated in veins like our own, but fills the tough envelope of the insect's body so that every organ is bathed in it. Then too, the method of breathing is utterly different. In order to aerate the blood, oxygen is not pumped through a special organ, the lungs, but through a network of fine tubes the tracheæ—which are all over the body in every limb and organ. These tubes are formed of rings between which oxygen escapes, and by the pressure of appropriate muscles it can be forced out of tube endings wherever it is needed. The air is admitted from outside through openings fitted with valves of various designs according to the species of insects, it enters the larger tubes which conduct it to the finest branches. On some muscles are minute spiral-shaped tubes to supply oxygen; these expand or contract with the muscle.

An insect's body consists of different segments joined together; each of these has a supply of blood, its own branches of air tubes, its own openings into the outer air closed by its own valves. Without being separated, each segment is more independent than it would be if there were local organs such as heart and lungs. The result of this system is that insects have a remarkable tenacity to life. Whereas an injury to heart or lungs would be fatal to members of other animal groups and to ourselves, an insect can survive by sealing up that part of the body so that the blood does not escape and then it can carry on as usual. It can be understood what a great chance of survival this ability can give.

I have known a praying mantis which escaped out of a spider's web leaving behind two out of its four walking legs—happily, one on each side—one of its predatory forelegs by which it traps living insects as food, and one antenna. I kept it for some time to see whether it could exist for long in that crippled state. I began by feeding it, catching insects and holding them near its mouth. That was no use; probably the whole digestive operation depended on the muscular exercise in catching insects for itself. It stared at the proffered food with opaque eyes but made no attempt to move its jaws. When I introduced living flies into its cage, it pursued them on two legs till it had a favourable position near them, caught them adroitly with its one foreleg, and really seemed very little inconvenienced by the loss of all these limbs. It was clumsy and sometimes fell but that was all. It did give me a surprise by forming a beautiful nest, rather below the normal size, but the eggs were laid without effort and they hatched. The spider had not bitten it. The lost limbs had got enmeshed when the mantis fell into the web with a struggling bee which it had just caught, and it was the mantis's own struggles which wrenched them off. There was one wound on the abdomen, and the fluid congealed on that at once. So there were no mortal hurts or what to an insect would impede its normal life. Injuries must be far more serious to have that result.

More surprising is the fact that a headless moth will lay her full number of eggs; perhaps most surprising of all is that a male will mate with her without worrying that part of her is missing. It is quite unnecessary to point out that anything comparable with these two examples cannot take place among mammals. And many more could be quoted. It is a definite advantage to have each segment of the body supplied with body fluid, muscles, nerves and oxygen.

The skin of an insect is worth more than a passing thought. It may be flexible as silk over some parts of

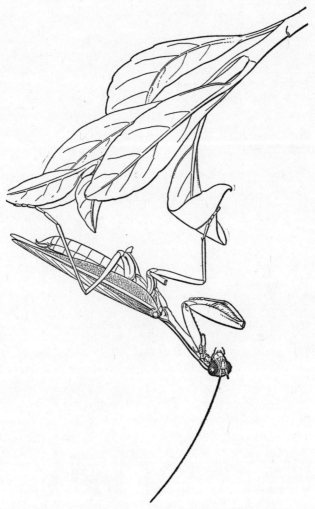

The crippled mantis continued to live

the body and in other parts tough or as hard as wood. Yet it is never one immovable suit of armour, because even the hardest is built up of plates joined by their membrane. The segments of a soft abdomen give it very free movements. This can be tested by holding a wasp or some other stinging insect by its wings and watching it turn and twist the abdomen in its efforts to sting. On one side the membranes between the plates will be stretched to their utmost capacity and on the other side neatly telescoped one under the next. The hard part of the body is a fusion of plates but most of the joints between are distinguishable.

Only the outermost part of the skin is one sheet. There are three layers compressed together, so it is best to examine a cross-section under a microscope to get a clear idea how it is formed. The top layer is a smooth and transparent substance—chitin. In most caterpillars and other larvæ this is all that is required; they remain soft until the next stage. When the mature insect first appears it may still be soft for a little while, but hardens after being in the air. Young ants and other insects as well may often be seen standing without movement for a while until the chitin has hardened.

Below the top skin the second layer is not one sheet, but is composed of cells which secrete the chitin. Below this, the third layer is membrane again, making a firm base for the cells.

All the clothing of insects, bristles, ordinary hairs,

feathery hairs, down and plush, grows out of the top skin. All are formed by being pushed up from the chitin and they are hollow inside. Quite a number of useful little instruments and tools are of chitin formed in the same way, knobs, thorns, spines, spurs, mounds and hollows. Some are toilet necessities, combs and brushes for cleaning delicate antennæ; some, like the praying mantis's strong spines, are for trapping and gripping insect victims. So they have all sorts of different functions yet all are merely protuberances of the outer skin.

Every hair grows singly from a minute pit and each is attached by a ring of membrane. The scales of a butterfly's wings which give them such beautiful colour patterns are all of chitin. They are like flattened hairs arranged very close together.

Special hairs develop in a different manner; they are sensory organs connected with nerves or they may be glandular connected with glands in the layer of cells. Many people have had the disagreeable surprise of being stung by a caterpillar. No caterpillar possesses a sting in the true sense of the word, it has no instrument to use in defence like the hymenoptera, the bees, wasps and ants, but if you handle a caterpillar with stinging hairs or if one should drop on you inadvertently inflammation may be set up or a spreading rash. The stinging hairs are called urticating—the reaction is very like that of stinging nettles—they are connected with glands in the lower layer of skin, and are always brittle and highly irritable. When they are touched, however lightly, fluid oozes out at the tip. Being sharp and very brittle, they enter a pore of the skin and the tip filled with irritant breaks off. This is why the affected part is often so painful. Yet you may not have been conscious that a caterpillar has dropped on you and then gone its way.

Still more specialized are the sensory hairs, each with a tiny nerve fibre which joins the main nerve system. They are very useful to an insect, informing it of all manner of things that it ought to know about.

The sensory hairs are on all parts of the body, especially on the feet, where they enlighten their owner as to the nature of what it is walking on, whether food or otherwise. So though the tactile organs can be so simple, just a piece of chitin pushed up from the skin and attached to a nerve, an insect depends upon them at all times to direct its actions so that the right set of nerves and muscles will be set in motion.

After a little practice, it is easy to guess a great deal about an insect by examining it through a pocket lens, how it lives, its food and much else of interest. A little knowledge opens up new lines of enquiry, so nobody need be bored in however isolated a spot he may happen to find himself because fortunately there are insects everywhere.

The shape of the legs usually furnishes a clue. Digging insects have broadened tips to the front pair of legs; or the whole foot, instead of being jointed, is a shovel-shaped tool for scooping out soil or rotten wood. Mole crickets have a delightful pair of trowels on the front legs, very broad, slightly hollowed and with strong teeth on the lower edge. A more fascinating little delver it is hard to imagine, and the speed with which it will tunnel away and disappear from sight if you catch one and put it on soft ground is amazing. It is curiously ungainly above ground or when blundering about in the air.

It is not everybody who will be thrilled with delight at seeing them work, because they certainly do a great deal of damage by burrowing right through the roots of delicate crops. It is seldom that one catches sight of them, as they work underground and fly at night, but they are attractive in their velvet waistcoats which never need brushing. If they can be induced to make a burrow in a glass tank against the side, you can watch them at work excavating and travelling about in the burrows.

Another very entertaining digger is the larva of the ant lion. Neat round pits in loose soil such as sand are very common, especially under the platforms of houses in the tropics where there is shelter from rain and probably an ants' nest nearby. Pits are formidable snares for ants and other insects, which slip over the edge and cannot save themselves. At the bottom lurks a peculiar grub with a shovel on its head. If the victim shows signs of escaping the shovel throws sand at it and brings it to the bottom again. When the victim has been sucked dry the empty skin is tossed clear of the pit by the same shovel. So the tool is used in more than one way.

Dig out one of these larvæ, set it on the ground and it disappears from view in a twinkling, levering up soil, inserting its soft hindquarters and then sinking in. It is such a tiny creature, only two or three millimetres long, yet the digging apparatus is most efficient.

Aquatic insects which have solved the problem of breathing air under water have done this by many different methods. There are some beautiful swimmers among them which dart about as swiftly as fish. Of them all perhaps the water boatmen are the most finished types. They have ugly habits and vulgar appetites. They feed on any soft-bodied creatures, larvæ of other insects, tadpoles and little fish, by piercing them with a fine proboscis and sucking out the contents of their bodies. But to watch boatmen swimming with their long strokes is a pleasure. They swim upside down and the whole body is shaped like a boat, flat on the underside which is turned upwards, and with a sort of keel on the upper side which is turned downwards. The legs are in exact proportion to take the weight, flattened and fringed with long, silky hairs that act like the blade of an oar. Two pairs of short legs are folded flat on the top of this little boat, but the hind legs reach beyond the end and so have a particularly long sweep propelling the body well forward with each sweep. The whole equipment is exquisite.

Air is evenly distributed in the boatman's body, but when the supply is exhausted it need not come outside the water to replenish it. You will notice that it rests against the surface underneath with only the ends of the air tubes through it. The valves open, take in the new supply, are closed again; then the boatman goes down to the bottom once more.

Other rather near relatives are the water skaters; they belong to the same order as the boatmen, but of quite a different shape, long-legged and thin. They can run about on the surface so freely because of the spread of those legs which exactly balances them. There are skaters on the open sea far from land, some which always keep near shore on coral reefs, many in strong currents of rivers and streams and others that are always found under waterfalls. So they are equipped for rough water. Those under the spray of waterfalls look as if they are deliberately courting danger. I have waded out expressly to watch them and it looked as if water was falling on them all the time as they bobbed and strode forward keeping their place on the swiftly moving current. Yet if these skaters are held underneath the water they will drown. Their oxygen equipment is velvet which holds tiny air bubbles and cannot be wetted; it covers body and legs. But if these bubbles get forced out of the velvet then they must drown.

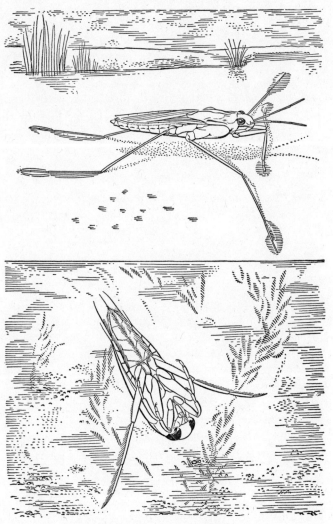

Aquatic and semi-aquatic insects

## The Elastic Body

The exact balance on the water film can be noted on a sunny day if you watch these skaters on a stream. The feet actually bend the water film and make little dimples, but they never fall through it. To pierce the film needs an effort. Skaters can run about on it; water boatmen and beetles, after flying about outside, have to close their air tubes and fold their wings, then struggle through the water film before they can swim. There is no diving through it, and some of the beetles can be seen kicking and struggling before they get their heads through it.

Mosquito larvæ have very simple vacuum pumps for their air supply, just tubes and some hairs which they push through the water film. They can be watched swinging themselves up to the surface to pump, and seem to need replenishing very often. Yet some can stay under water for the whole winter without needing air. Those which I had once under observation had not appeared for a whole month, so I emptied their tank to see what had become of them. They had anchored themselves to weeds by tiny hooks, and were hanging head downwards with closed air tubes and suspended activities until the change of season took place.

The little hooks were only needed for that occasion. Often tools that are part of the equipment disappear when a change takes place and they are not needed any longer. Thus the blow-fly is kept safe when a pupa in a hard chitinous shell, but when the time comes for it to emerge it has a special little organ for softening the chitin to let it out, to pick the lock of its own front door. Then this organ and its fluid disappear because the adult fly does not on any occasion use such a tool again.

There are odd structures among the extravagant forms whose use is not so easy to guess as the periscope of the small grasshoppers. Some of the flies have branched processes near the eyes—the stag-horned flies—which are very ornamental but one would imagine a little cumbersome, and nobody can suggest their use. Hover flies have very long hairs with a knob at the end. Then there are the stalk-eyed flies, a peculiar little group. These have a habit of sitting on the edge of a leaf with only the eyes visible, but whether there can be any advantage to a fly in being able to look round the corner is not very obvious. But all the extravagant forms are worth examining because they show the many directions in which an insect's body can vary.

# 2. *Senses*

It would naturally be expected that insects' sense organs, which inform them of everything that is important in their own little lives, must be different from those of the animal world in general and from those of human beings in particular. Yet when we begin to study insects' sense organs it is rather difficult to avoid trying to find comparisons with our own. One ought to start off firmly with the realization that there is very little analogy. If we appreciate that fact from the outset then the beauty of their efficiency is far more apparent.

The essential point is that the sense organs are perfect instruments for conveying to the insect exclusively what most concerns it. Insects have eyes and can see, some with more definition than others. But their vision and their eyes are not like ours and what they see does not convey the same meaning to them as to us. They have organs to register vibrations. We may call them ears but they are not in the least comparable to our highly developed organs of hearing. They can hear everything which concerns them and there is an enormous variety of designs to register what is significant to each insect group—warning of enemies, indication of prey, or of their own mates and so on. But on the other hand although the number of vibrations per second which the human ear can register are said to be as many as 30,000, the insect's simple organ may receive vibrations which we are incapable of hearing and very few of those 30,000.

Some little male grasshoppers may be watched while they are fiddling—stridulating—to attract their mates. We can see the movement as they rub a rough surface of the legs against the side of the body but we hear no sound. Yet we know that those grasshoppers must be sending out sound waves because we can see the females come to answer the call.

Stridulating organs take various forms. When we find a patch of ridges on an insect's body or little tubercles, on some grubs as well as mature insects, we can recognize these as some kind of stridulator used with some other part to make friction. But we may not be able to hear the sounds which they make. So all the insects round about us might be making sounds which are imperceptible except to one another.

Many moths can stridulate. There are certain butterflies which make a click with their wings which can be distinctly heard. But the whole air may be ringing with sounds made by insects and we can be only conscious of a few of them, such as buzzing of flies and humming of bees and wasps.

As for insects' sense of smell through their olfactory organs, although these are very simple compared with our highly developed noses, scent is an immensely powerful directive for many insects, and we have ample proof that they can detect numberless things which for us have no scent and also that they can perceive scent from a very long distance away.

As we can smell only a comparatively limited range of scents we have to be cautious, when watching insects, about how we decide whether they are being guided by sight or by scent. In a great many cases it is impossible to decide without making tests. Then also we do not know whether they use touch or taste in selecting their food.

Moreover, insects have other sense organs to which we cannot even put a name because they are not analogous to anything we possess ourselves and we cannot guess how they function. Now that we are familiar with radio we think it possible that insects may intercommunicate by some kind of etheric wave transmission. Perhaps they may also possess a sense like that of water diviners. And we must frankly own that they may receive sensations which no human being can translate at all.

So to come back to the original point, it is necessary to disabuse ourselves entirely of the notion that we can judge the sensations which an insect receives by our own sensations. It is something quite different from anything we have ever felt, and that is all we know. We may think that an insect sees or smells an object when all that has happened is that a bristle on its foot has conveyed some sort of information. We have no bristles on our feet that will do the same, the nearest analogy is a cat's whiskers and that is not identical.

Altogether it is an enthralling subject, some of the research on it has been extremely ingenious—most requiring surgical operations—and has resulted in some delightful discoveries.

Over two hundred years ago an Italian scientist interested himself in the buzz of mosquitoes. He knew that the irritating ping-ping is made by the vibration of mosquitoes' wings, and he had come to the conclusion that the lovely antennæ like a feathery headdress which some male mosquitoes wear was not an ornament but a receiving instrument for sound. The female wears a pair of processes but they are not so elaborate. Now he had to invent some method for testing his theory, and it had to be carried out on living insects which added to difficulties.

The first operation was to keep a male mosquito in a certain position. So he caught one and carefully tethered it with a piece of fine silk without injuring it in any way, leaving its head free to move in all directions. Next he took tuning forks and tried every tone, holding the forks, one at a time, in front of the mosquito. When he had managed to reproduce the high-pitched buzz some of the fibrils began to move. By moving the tuning fork farther to the front all fibrils were affected and some on the other antenna began to move. When the fork was exactly opposite, all fibrils on the pair of antennæ were vibrating fully. This was a highly satisfactory result and it was later checked by other research. The buzz of the female mosquito is the call to its mate. The male of each species has this special apparatus for responding to the female of his own species. If part of his receiving apparatus is in motion, that signifies that a female is somewhere in his neighbourhood. When he has moved his head into a position so that the full blast of vibrations is received he can then fly straight in her direction and find her. Any other noises that happened to surround that male mosquito—people talking, a brass band, farmyard animals giving tongue, a disturbed wasps' nest, any other disturbance of the air that would fill it with a medley of vibrations—would make not the slightest difference to the suitor. He would fly unerringly to the spot where his lady was signalling, for no other sound would be registered to disconcert him.

On the female mosquito's head upon the antennæ is a sensory organ of another description which the male does not need. This is to aid her in discriminating between the subtle differences of the water in which her eggs are to be laid. Mosquito larvæ will only thrive in water which has certain conditions that are necessary for different species. They are specially adapted for living and finding their food under these special conditions. Some can only live in fresh water, others can survive in slightly saline water and so have the advantage of less competition. Some live in stagnant water, some in slow currents, others in swift currents. Some live in a small quantity of rain-water collected in plants or tree holes.

Even tree holes offer quite different conditions. Some have clear water, others are full of dead leaves. Some contain besides rain-water the oozing sap of the tree. I have found mosquitoes breeding in water in *Araucaria* trees so thick with resin that it looked like stout and I had to dilute it with water before I could see the larvæ. So there are very many conditions and the larvæ are adapted to find their food in one only, therefore the responsibility for selecting the right conditions rests upon the female's sense organs.

During the First World War there was some anxiety

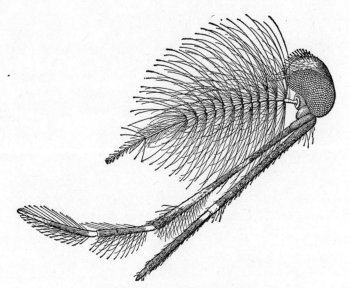

Antennæ of male mosquito

Antennæ of female mosquito

in England lest malaria should be introduced through soldiers returning from tropical countries with their blood infected. Malaria which used to be known as ague had died out in England, but there are three species of mosquitoes which it was thought might become carriers of the disease if they bit these soldiers but happily this did not take place.

All kinds of research was carried out in England and some of it was connected with recording all the conditions of different types of water in which mosquitoes could breed. The apparatus for testing the constituents of water consisted mainly of different chemicals to give different colour reactions. The testing apparatus was heavy and cumbersome with all the chemical reagents and all the samples in test-tubes. When different types of nets and basins were added it was as much as a man could manage to test the water in a few localities in one day.

Yet the female mosquito can carry out her tests with the greatest accuracy, rejecting some situations and only laying her eggs if she gets the exact reaction required. But the whole of her special outfit for that important duty is a microscopic sensory organ on her antennæ.

They are entirely automatic—these reactions on the female's part to something which guides her in selecting favourable conditions for the next generation. But whatever they are, they have become agents because the mosquito has evolved a sensory organ to respond to them—otherwise they could not affect her. An interesting test of this which it is possible for anybody to carry out is a trick we can play on the common white cabbage butterflies.

The female butterfly selects plants of the cabbage family on which the caterpillars feed. But if mustard oil is sprinkled on any other kind of plant she will still lay her eggs on it being guided by her olfactory organ.

I have experimented with dock leaves which have no scent appreciable to the human nose, leaves of aromatic plants, red leaves, yellow leaves, and holly. The result in every case was the same. The butterflies attached their eggs to any leaf that had the scent to which the olfactory organ responded, quite oblivious to the fact that the caterpillars would not be able to feed and would starve to death.

Scent is very important to an insect in the dense tropical growth of forests. *Euploea* is a butterfly that keeps almost entirely to shade. Both sexes will be seen floating about languidly on their velvet wings in deep shadows. Because they lack a distinctive colour pattern only the movement may betray them—at least to human eyes. The wings are pitch black with one or two minute white spots in some species. No doubt the dark colouring is of value to these butterflies in protecting them from enemies. But the male has a tiny brush connected with a scent gland which can be protruded or withdrawn into the end of the body. This delicate organ atomizes the secretion as he sits patiently on a leaf with the body upturned. The female which may be a long way off in the depths of the vegetation or in the tree tops receives the sensation through her olfactory organ and finds her mate without loss of time and energy.

One of the many interesting experiments on hive bees was to find out where their olfactory organ was situated. It was considered that this was on the antennæ but the fact had not been proved. The experiment lasted for some time but was entirely convincing. A number of little porcelain boxes were arranged on a table not far away from bee hives and soon some workers got into the habit of visiting them daily. Some of these were caught and marked so that they could be watched individually. Three of the boxes were empty, one had an oil which gave out a strong scent like flowers and one had only sugar in solution. It was found that wherever the perfumed oil was placed the bees found it at once; the position would be changed often but they wasted no time. This suggested that they were guided by their olfactory organ because they would visit the sugar as well but not the empty boxes.

After these marked bees had been thoroughly accustomed to search for either of those two boxes their antennæ were amputated. They came as before, arrived at the table and did not appear disturbed by the operation but their behaviour was different, for they could not locate the oil box and went into the empty boxes as often as into the one with sugar. This had not happened before, they had not taken any interest in the empty boxes but now that the olfactory organs had been removed they were directed by sight only.

Other worker bees were allowed to habituate themselves to colour in association with scent. Blue paper covered the sugar box, some of the others were yellow. Thanks to their memory, after several days they associated blue with sugar so that when their antennæ were amputated it made no difference to them. They were relying on sight instead of scent.

But insects' olfactory organs are not only in the antennæ. They have other organs responding to scent, so experiments do not always have such definite results as in the case quoted of the hive bees. Carrion beetles which lay their eggs in decaying animal matter have been known to find meat buried in sand even without their antennæ and wings and with their legs covered in shellac to inhibit any organ which might be on them. Some sense guided them but how they detected the meat cannot be decided. Perhaps some faculty of meat-divination was used. In the absence of facts we fall back on conjecture but that proves nothing.

It is possible that certain aquatic insects possess an extra sense for finding water. So many of them arrive at night, and it is remarkable how very quickly a new pool of water will be populated by all sorts of aquatic insects. It was concluded at one time that the aquatic beetles can see reflected light from the water and that it is this which guides them, for even on moonless nights there may be a very faint glimmer from stars if the sky is not overcast.

This conclusion is based on human sensations. If we wanted to find water we should be guided by sight and a blind man would fail to find it. To these aquatic insects water is a prime necessity so those insects will be better equipped for the task of finding it. But not enough research has been carried out on this subject to warrant any more than guesses.

I have known a pit in a brickyard begin to seep water one afternoon, and at midday on the following day I saw in it three species of water beetles and one species of water skaters though the water had only half filled the pit. In some cases too the new pool may be a very dark tree hole in the depths of tropical forest. I have marked one hollow which formed at the roots of a huge tree after gales had brought down another tree on the top of it. I had to creep under a thick screen of interlacing branches and even by daylight it was dark there. Next morning at dawn there was a water beetle and a water boatman in that pool. They must have arrived in the dark. There was a mosquito too, a female walking about near the surface testing general conditions.

Mosquitoes fly low in among trees but I have never seen aquatic beetles or any of the aquatic bugs such as the water boatmen flying in among the vegetation. They make for open spaces, may fly above the tree tops and are not attracted to lights at night except on very rare occasions. So it does not seem probable that these insects are searching near the ground for water. It is more likely that they get their information by some sense organ other than their eyes. It may be that the olfactory organs come into play for this work or some water-divining organ whose functions are still undiscovered.

Experiments on insects' eyes brought to light a great deal of interesting information. There are many quite different types of eyes among insects, some of which depend upon sight far more than others. There are simple eyes consisting of one lens and compound eyes which may have hundreds. Hymenoptera may have both types—at the sides of the head the most highly developed eyes and at the top of the head simple ones which can discriminate between light and dark and may be of use in dark burrows. Whirligig beetles have double eyes. When they are skimming about on the top of water the upper half of their eyes sees any prey which has fallen on the surface and the lower half sees under the water. So little escapes their notice.

Wonderful results followed research on glow-worms' eyes. The first experiment was in Vienna carried out by an Austrian scientist, Dr. Exner. He used the eye like a miniature camera. He put a drop of gelatine behind it and photographed with it. The result astonished everyone taking part in that research. A large letter R had been cut out of white paper and pasted on to a window-pane. The camera was turned toward this, but not only did the letter R appear distinctly when the photograph was developed but actually a little distant view of trees and a church spire. Definition was not sharp but the objects could be recognized. Experiments were repeated in England. One portrait was made of a professor's head in silhouette which was unmistakable. The unexpected fact which emerged was that the eyes of the more highly developed insect can set up an image of what is unimportant in its life as well as objects which concern it intimately. The nerves of the eye will not register them and the nerve memory will not retain them. Butterflies can see well at a short distance so are guided helpfully to a flower bed and may return to it next day. But the garden gate has no interest though the eyes are capable of giving a tolerably clear image of it which human eyes could recognize.

Dragonflies have the best sight of all. This is because their eyes have an immense number of lenses. The slightest movement within their perimeter of vision will be perceived more quickly than by most insects. Perhaps it is because they have such keen sight that the forest-hunting species seem to find one another without difficulty. They are not endowed with scent glands and brushes for this task, and some have very little colour pattern which is an advantage when hunting their prey.

Some with long slender bodies and delicate gauzy wings are almost invisible in shadow. One light spot at the end of the abdomen like the lamp at the end of a train may be seen moving about mysteriously, and some have a pattern near the eyes. The insect on a leaf may see nothing but those three marks which—to a human eye— would suggest three small wandering flies, but the dragonfly's mate is attracted to it.

To prove which sense is being used by an insect the other senses have to be put out of action. Some curious experiments were made on field crickets. There was a lot of preparation as in most research on insects. Some little cages were made and males and females were kept out of sight of one another but were connected by telephones. It can be well understood that all outside vibrations had to be carefully eliminated before a test was made. But when this had been done and males began to chirrup, watch was kept on the females on the other end of the telephones to see whether they showed signs of receiving the sound. It was known that they have well-developed auditory organs but their function had to be confirmed.

There was a most satisfactory response, the females crowded close to the receivers in their cages. And when the organ of hearing was removed, which acts like a tympanum of our own ears, it was found that those doctored females made no movement while the others were crowding to the spot whence the male voice proceeded. So here again we have very good evidence on the function of that organ.

The invention of the supersonic whistle shows the existence of many airwaves of frequencies which react upon animals and insects but not on ourselves. There was an extremely ingenious invention in the United States for testing the olfactory organs of the dreaded potato beetle. It was called an olfactometer and consisted of glass tubes shaped like a "Y." The beetles entered the stem and were given the choice of an empty branch or a branch containing the essence of the potato, and afterwards in another test the essence of the chopped-up leaves of the plant. The originator recorded the reactions of a number of beetles at different stages of their lives and in different months of the year. He also recorded that he could not himself detect any scent from the plants although he could from the potato. The beetles were responsive after mating but not always before. This is an interesting point. But they one and all rejected the empty branch and crowded into the other whether the scent was of plants or tubers.

Butterflies have a very good colour vision, which implies nerve memory as well as good eyesight, for when mating it is the chief directive. All sorts of experiments have been made and some kinds of butterflies are more easily taken in than others, it appears. Yellow butterflies related to the cabbage whites came readily to paper models if of the exact colour of their mates and seemed very puzzled by the lack of response to their advances. Fritillaries seemed more discriminating. When very well painted photographs were put up on trees and bushes where a number of these butterflies were about, and with them some dead fritillaries, the butterflies rejected the paper ones after swooping down for a near view but were interested in the dry specimens until they found them singularly unresponsive and then these too were rejected. Of course it is possible that the fritillaries were using some sense other than sight.

Living butterflies of any species may often be noticed chasing some specimen which is not related but has the same coloration though not exactly the same pattern. It is the colour which attracts them undoubtedly. Then a nearer inspection shows them their error.

Bees of course carry in memory the colour of the particular flowers which they are visiting regularly. A bumble bee which had been very busy on sunflowers was seen to fly to a pet parrot and make a casual inspection of its lemon-coloured breast which happened to be of the exact tone of the sunflowers.

Those little wasps which make use of any hole of the right size that will suit their requirements for a burrow must certainly carry an image in memory of what they seek. I have amused myself many a time by painting a hole on paper and hanging it up on the wall to see how often a wasp will be deceived. In this case it is the nature of the shadowed entrance which is conveyed to the insect, and anything which suggests that comes in for a conscientious examination each time a newcomer appears on the scene. But I have seen one wasp start the hunting on the same wall after she had finished—I suppose in case she had missed one hole—but she did not inspect the faked holes a second time.

What must surprise anybody who lives near large woodlands is the way certain beetles are aware in a very short time that a tree has been felled. It is of course those beetles that feed on certain trees which receive the information that one is ready for them. They have to pair and the female lays eggs inside the timber by the help of her ovipositor. When the grubs hatch they will feed on the wood. Such beetles do not attack the living tree but come to a felled trunk. When collecting beetles it is always worth while to take a light on the first night after a felling and examine the bark, for weevils and other kinds of beetles will probably be there already.

There is a very handsome dark blue longicorn beetle with an emerald pattern which is addicted to chestnut trees. Once when on Tahiti in the mountains I heard a continuous humming which sounded like a swarm of bees. I made my way to a glade where men had that morning felled a huge chestnut, a mapé tree. The glade was alive with flying beetles of this species. It was an astonishing sight. They were coming in scores from every direction and running about on the trunk. The whole of their business was being transacted very rapidly. They flew down and paired, then the female, which has a rather short ovipositor, found a crack and laid her eggs in it. Perhaps the search for a suitable crack was the longest operation. I had been collecting for some time in that neighbourhood and on that day had caught only five of these beetles. They are daylight, sun-loving beetles and like to drink nectar from flowers. They may have been on the flowering crowns of trees out of sight.

But here they were crowded. I counted thirty on one bough and the humming from their wings could be heard from some distance away. What struck one as almost magical was their appearance on a tree so recently felled that the leaves were only beginning to wilt in the sun. It must have been the scent from those which attracted them or else from the timber where it had been chopped. And the scent of either of them must have been widely diffused to result in such a staggering assembly.

One could continue almost interminably to quote examples of this description. Sufficient has been given however to illustrate the exquisite efficiency of these minute sense organs. And those who are interested in the subject will find hundreds of records of a similar nature in our scientific literature.

# 3. Protective Devices

The DISCOVERY OF MIMICRY AMONG IN-sects started a new subject with new lines of investigation. It is a very absorbing subject with bypaths which lead us into a maze at times, and new examples are always being discovered.

There are various grades of mimicry, the most perfect give such attention to detail that even with the model and its mimic before you it is necessary to look very carefully to discover the disguise. Others can be separated after a cursory inspection, yet could be passed over as bearing such a general resemblance that they would both be taken for the same species. The same coloration is what catches the eye and an enemy searching for something different would leave the mimic alone.

That is the main incentive for this perplexing develop-

ment, the mimic in so many cases is not so well protected from enemies as the model, so by mimicry de-
ludes its enemies into avoiding it. This explanation has
been so universally accepted, and is so plain in the
majority of cases, that when a new example comes to
light it is assumed that the model must have some
sort of advantage worth copying even if that is not
always evident.

Bold design and conspicuous colours give an immunity which can be recognized anywhere. It is known
as warning coloration. Red and yellow are warning
colours, any insect sporting these will be avoided by
birds, lizards and other insectivorous creatures. But
among them are many mimicking insects which gain
decided advantage by having these colours. The stinging insects, bees and wasps, have all manner of mimics.
These are wasp-like flies and beetles and bee-like flies
and moths. Most of these have habits which are clearly
adaptations to make them still more like the models,
habits which are not practised by their own relatives.

Some of the parasites mimic their hosts. It can be
seen that such disguises are very useful for getting into
private quarters. The little stingless bees can defend
their nests for they have formic acid glands connected
with the mandibles and can give a bite which is respected
by anything of their size. But one of their chief parasites
is a small fly which mimics the bees in every particular
and thus manages to get into nests by flying in with

the worker bees. There are many other parasitic mimics, and it will be noticed that the new habits play an important part in helping this disguise.

The tropics produce the greatest number of mimetic forms and it was the work of two great naturalists, Bates on the Amazon, and Belt in Nicaragua, which first drew the attention of the scientific world to this most interesting subject. When their two fascinating books, *The Naturalist on the Amazon,* by Bates, and *The Naturalist in Nicaragua,* by Belt, were published the general public became interested. Darwin, Wallace, Müller added very important studies.

Following on the idea that well-protected insects were mimicked came the discovery that some butterflies have mimics belonging to other families, some moths too mimic certain butterflies. It was proved that these models were usually avoided as food and that led to the conclusion that certain insects had juices obnoxious to the usual enemies, which would make them quite as useful models as insects with stings. Research was carried out to test the theory and so many cases were proved that it had a general acceptance. Tests under unnatural conditions do not always turn out as expected, but many considerations have to be taken into account, for instance birds in captivity will often accept as edible out of boredom what they might avoid as risky. But if anything hesitates to try experiments with a mimic that very fact gives it immunity.

Some caterpillars exude a waxy secretion which is thought to be a protection. Such caterpillars make themselves conspicuous sitting quite openly on foliage, which suggests that they possess something of protective value or they would have the habit of concealment like most caterpillars.

One would imagine that even a young inexperienced bird, if it snatched at this fat morsel and had a beakful of wax, would not make a second trial. I wanted confirmation of this point and while I was Curator of Insects in the London Zoo I bred out some caterpillars purposely and tried them on an Australian kookaburra. He pounced eagerly on the first caterpillar then threw it out again with plain signs of disgust, but tackled another one with the same result and a third which he swallowed complacently. This seemed to have no ill effects and he applied himself to the rest so zealously that I had to remove them as I wanted some for other experiments.

We can assume that with other choice of food those caterpillars would have been avoided, but as a cage does not offer the amenities of forest the bird was prepared to make an experiment. But the theory cannot be accepted in its entirety; there are exceptions.

Monarch butterflies are thought to have distasteful juices. With their conspicuous yellow and tawny wing pattern they can never conceal themselves. Their flight is very leisurely, altogether their behaviour does not suggest that they have enemies to avoid. One never sees them attacked, nor are their caterpillars popular as food. Yet on one island of the New Hebrides a kingfisher was feeding its young with them. Perhaps food happened to be scarce in that neighbourhood, but the nestlings were not refusing them as was proved by the numbers of wings on the ground below the nest. So we can assume that in special circumstances birds or others can accustom themselves to an insect which has immunity from most of its enemies.

The clearwing moths have no scales like other moths so their transparent wings look very like that of a bee. When they hover over a flower the wings make a vibration that can be heard from a short distance away. But there semblance goes no further than the furry body and clear wings, the veins of the wings are not the same, the sound they make is not actually a humming, and of course the long proboscis unrolled to dip into the flower betrays it—at least to human eyes.

Butterfly mimics have been studied intensively. It was found that some have two broods, seasonal broods of dry and rainy seasons. One brood may be a mimic and not the next, so there will be marked difference in broods of the same species. Directly these facts were known entomologists began to look through their collections more carefully, and found numbers of butterflies or moths which had been arranged unnoticed among their models. Differences will be seen on looking into the pattern. In the model, pattern will be close to the veins, while in mimics sometimes it overlaps them or is less sharply defined or less symmetrical. Many butterflies, and especially moths, have as part of the pattern translucent zones like little windows. The mimics have evolved something that looks very like a window but it is false, the colour makes it look translucent.

One species of beetle has produced a wonderful mimic of a hunting wasp. The wings of beetles and wasps are so different, the former has few veins and the latter a delicate network of them, and in this model there is a vivid white stripe which the mimic has represented beautifully. As a beetle keeps its wings hidden and this wasp is in the habit of running about with its wings widespread the mimicry would not be so exact if this habit too had not been evolved. So the beetle too spreads its wings, which is a most unusual position. The wasps have a slender waist and beetles none but the mimic has light patches at the side of the body in the middle which give the illusion of a waist.

If an insect that looks like a wasp sits on a trunk with wings outspread showing the familiar white bar nobody is going to molest it, for these wasps can give a very painful sting. The mimics are usually found to be less active, they deceive by keeping in one position. When they walk about one can spot differences.

There is a tiger beetle with a wonderful mimic. The beetle is a fantastic creature that runs round trees, and then puts a gnomish face round the side of a trunk to watch your next movement as a squirrel will do. In the Philippine Islands there is a cricket which mimics this beetle. To do this its race had to evolve a sharp diversion from those nearly related—a remarkable accomplishment. Both model and mimic pass most of their lives on trees, so it is a very helpful disguise because they are often found together.

Some of the bugs in their early stages mimic ants. The differences are relatively slight but effective. The bugs run about near ant trails and spear ants and other small insects and probably escape the usual dangers from their own enemies.

In all these examples of mimicry even entomologists who study small characters may be taken in, so that birds, lizards, mice which are not conscious of such characters as the shape of the antennæ will not risk trying to eat something which suggests a sting or a nasty flavour.

Ladybirds as a group are protected by a nasty flavour. Their gaudy patterns are recognized and therefore they are avoided. They have many mimics in different orders of insects. In this question of whether an insect has an obnoxious taste we can only judge by the behaviour of its enemies. An enthusiastic entomologist has been known to taste caterpillars in order to find out whether he could detect a difference in flavour; but the human palate is not comparable to that of a lizard or a mouse, it would refuse many things which they enjoy.

Camouflage is brought to the finest art. Mimicry of static things, leaves, twigs, lichen, moss, bark, are perfect. Twig caterpillars have instincts to match the disguise. They have smooth bodies with knobs or buds. If they took up the wrong position these would be of no use to them. They can be watched selecting a spot with great precision, touching a twig on each side, then posing between them and at the right angle. It is a consummate disguise which on one occasion at least earned a valuable testimony. For I watched a moth actually lay its eggs on the false bud. It walked up and down the caterpillar several times, but nothing raised suspicion, the caterpillar remained as still as a rock. This may often occur. Either the caterpillar has the scent of a twig or the moth is guided by some other sense.

Leaf mimicry is well known. That too has its finishing touches. Grasshoppers and their relations the leaf insects are the best known leaf mimics. The colour of the insect will change with the leaves as the season advances and edges will look brown and dry or patches like fungus may appear.

Lichen mimicry is beautiful among moths with the habit of sitting on bark. Not only the colours but the actual form of lichen is reproduced with dark lines that look like shadows. Some kinds of praying mantis have patterns on the wings which help them to blend

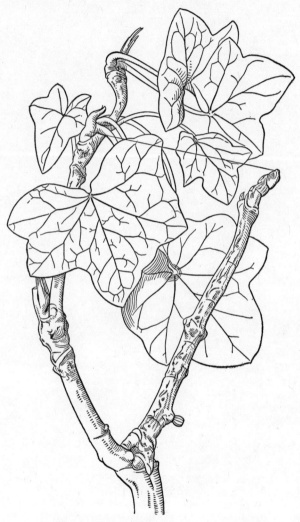

The twig caterpillar deceived a moth

with foliage, and outgrowths of the body or legs which break up the lines and make them quite difficult to detect, especially green ones. A group of leaf buds, twigs and a thorny spike may suddenly introduce itself as all belonging to one insect. This serves as camouflage against enemies but equally well to deceive their prey. Flower mimicry too is carried out among mantids. They have coloured expansions which exactly resemble petals, and as flowers offer excellent strategic positions for waylaying insects this camouflage serves them well.

Some pattern which breaks up the outline of an insect is a very useful adaptation; in caterpillars this is often noticed. There is a conspicuous design when you hold them in your hand, but among the lights and shades it will pass unnoticed so long as it has not got the usual contour. One little caterpillar which showed an unusual form that would deceive human beings was very like a snail. It was in the same bushes as a peculiar jumping snail of New Guinea and attracted my attention because it seemed to be walking backwards and did not jump when disturbed. The front part is very much swollen and at first glance would be taken for a snail shell. If this is a case of mimicry one would expect helpful habits to be evolved to improve the deception. Either the hind part of the body should have taken this marble-like form or else the caterpillar should walk backwards. But that is to see the matter from a human viewpoint. Certainly they did not suggest the idea of caterpillars and that is the main objective, to protect them from birds and lizards.

The theory on the origin of species which is known as Darwinism was considered for some time to be a satisfactory solution for some of these mystifying problems in nature—especially in the insect world which has illustrated what an immense number of totally different forms may be evolved from one stem. It is a fact that insects arose out of simpler forms, but they have existed from such ancient times that there are no truly archaic forms for comparison. And insects do not make good fossils.

But what can have been the forces which caused them to split up into innumerable species? When the subject of mimics and models gained prominence, a great volume of thought was directed to the subject of what looks like purposive deception being carried out exquisitely by creatures that are no more than automatons.

Working independently, Charles Darwin and Alfred Russell Wallace came to the same conclusion, although later scientists modified this theory: that it was the pressure of outside circumstances—enemies, change of climate, competition over the same food, etc.—which caused variations, and that if these were favourable to a species the race that evolved them would survive and others without such advantage would be wiped out. It was a case of survival of the fittest, said these two scientists. In a case of mimicry, they argued, a variation which was a little like a fortunate model would increase the mimic's chances, and by steady elimination of all those which did not vary enough—natural selection—the most sucessful races of that group would survive.

Climates have changed all over the globe. Certain groups of insects might develop some advantage which would help them to stand the new conditions. As to the pressure of enemies, any colour or form which made detection difficult would be characters inherited by the next generation. Any variation which was a hindrance would not be inherited.

Darwin wrote, "The chick which cannot break the egg-shell, the caterpillar that fails to suspend itself properly or to spin a safe cocoon, the bees that lose their way or that fail to store honey—inevitably perish. So the birds that fail to feed and protect their young, or the butter-flies that lay their eggs on the wrong foodplant—leave no offspring and the race with imperfect instincts per-ishes.

"Now, during the long and very slow course of de-velopment of each organism, this rigid selection at every step of progress has led to the preservation of every de-tail of structure, faculty or habit that has been necessary for the preservation of the race, and has thus gradually built up the various instincts which seem so marvellous to us, but which can be shown to be in many cases still imperfect."

There was serious opposition to this theory of natural selection as the origin of species, though nobody could come forward with more convincing arguments. It was gradually accepted by most scientists as the most satisfactory explanation that could be put forward, and some were even enthusiastic over it. Until Darwin's death it was considered by the majority of thinkers that he had cut the Gordian Knot and that scientists could go forward building on that theory. Well-deserved appreciation was given to Darwin as a master brain; his lucid arguments and his delightful experiments made his books popular. Wallace's contributions too were studied by everybody, and Müller's.

Then in the years that followed came a reversion of ideas, which found weak points in their arguments, and other interpretations to what had been quoted to illustrate their points. This change of thought was started by far greater research on the cell, the nucleus which develops into an organism by specialized cells. Something of the utmost importance has been discovered recently, that variations which appear to take place suddenly have actually been preparing gradually in each generation, until the last rearrangement produces a visible variation which may make an insect appear very different from its parents. For this is what had been the chief puzzle. If subtle variations led up to forms such as the exquisite mimics, how is it that we do not find many intermediate forms? It was this which scientists sought to explain by the wiping out of those not perfect enough to deceive. Yet, if all were wiped out how could the mimics have been evolved? Now we know that these may not have been members of intermediate forms. Chromosomes were discovered too to have a greater part to play than had been realized. So gradually it was accepted that the power to vary is within, that the organism itself has unconscious control over its own variations, and is not forced into specific development by outside forces. In other words, a race has an unconscious ideal and develops towards it.

It seems very unfair to Darwin that he himself should be discredited by some people and his work underrated. It is most unfortunate that the great theorists of this world should attract a following of disciples who make dogmas of their theories and so give them a character which was never intended. In almost any instance it is not the original thinker who is dogmatic but those who take it on themselves to expound his theory. Later generations forget this, and blame the author as though he purposely misled them by propounding a tenet as though it were indisputable.

Of all men Darwin has least deserved this at our hands for he was assuredly never dogmatic. Even though he accepted his own theory of natural selection as the only solution of the problem he wrote in the summary of his book on the origin of species—"The theory of natural selection seems to be in the highest degree probable. . . . I have already recapitulated as fairly as I could the opposed difficulties and objections."

Indeed we can be quite sure that Darwin would never have been a Darwinist. He would have been one of the first to accept any modification of his arguments in the light of additional evidence. His life work was the collecting of evidence to prove the law of evolution which he established beyond doubt, one of the few laws in biology which is accepted as proved. When he attempted to discover the *cause* of new species both he and Wallace concluded that they arose through some sort of variation produced by a change in their immediate environment.

The point has certainly not been reached where anybody dares to dogmatize, for any day may bring forth the discovery of new evidence to throw an unexpected light on some aspect of the problems. But this much we can accept, that the development of certain characters depends upon the relationship between the factor which is contained in a chromosome and the surrounding material—the protoplasm. But if some change takes place in this relationship then the character will vary. Outside influences such as Darwin called "blind agents" can affect a race but only if the inner directive is as it were linked up with that which is outside it so that it becomes a stimulus.

By interbreeding and selection man has influenced the production of all kinds of variations from the stock, but we have only brought uppermost the variations which were inherent in the race. Look at all the dog breeds produced from the wolf, but man cannot breed dogs with horns or cloven feet because that line of variation is not inherent in the wolf.

To return to the illustration of a pack of cards. Some races possess a larger pack than others but no pressure from outside will make them produce something which is not in their pack, and we have many examples of some card being turned uppermost which seems to us to have no utility to the race that displays it.

A great many very interesting experiments have been made to try to force insects to adopt new food plants. It was hoped by such tests to make them form habits and produce variations which were alien to their race, and by selection and breeding to prove that they can inherit the newly acquired characters. But it cannot be said that any evidence of this has been recorded.

What was made clear and is in itself a very interesting fact is that certain insects may readily accept a new diet until they finally reject their original food. But when it comes to passing on this preference, which would mean that it had become fixed as a new habit, the experiments break down. Usually the failure has been on account of the female, which refuses to lay eggs on any plant except the normal food of her ancestors although as a caterpillar she was feeding on the new diet. Or, in cases where the female has gone so far along the new route, the brood has not succeeded in reaching maturity.

The majority of these experiments were carried out on what are called biological races, which are races that feed on one particular plant but show no outward difference in colour or pattern from those that feed on other plants. They are not different species, any males will mate with females of the other biological race. There may be some minute inner difference, probably in the female's sense organs.

There were good experiments on some sawflies which form galls on willows, and some of the results brought surprises. One race was taken away from its own willow and transported to a district where several different species of willow were growing including its own. There it selected another species and ignored what had seemed its speciality. Therefore it is probable that those sawflies accustom themselves to a willow in a district where only that exists but would adopt another species if they had the choice.

All these questions can only be settled by experiments and then more experiments, to prove the deductions arrived at. And entomologists must not be allowed to crystallize an idea, but must keep an open mind on the subject or even be prepared to abandon it altogether—perhaps a life's work—if disproved by further investigations.

# 4. Dispersal and Migration

THERE IS A TENDENCY IN THESE DAYS TO discard some of our old theories upon the cause of insect migrations. Why, for example, should some kinds of locusts leave an area in such vast multitudes that the sky is darkened and fly halfway round the world before they are satisfied?

When scientists first began to study the subject it was decided that there must be some pressure of circumstances, some hitch in domestic arrangements to cause it. It was noticed that some insect migrations start in years when a species has multiplied beyond its normal numbers. Therefore it was only natural to suppose that the urge to migrate results from over-population causing food shortage, too keen a competition for necessities, lack of sufficient space and so forth. They saw the matter from a human viewpoint. Had there not been mass migration of human beings caused by the same needs? So that theory was held for some time.

There are many insects which migrate regularly. In nearly every order of insects some races are true migrants. We find migrants among butterflies and moths, beetles, dragonflies, and other groups not so widely known. Many are so small that their migrations are not noticeable, unless they damage our crops, then we get evidence of their movements over long distances, and research has shown up some very curious facts.

Then it was discovered that immense numbers of insects are airborne which are not migrating, but are carried by strong winds. It was considered that these were caught unawares and transported involuntarily. From the time that this was first noticed all kinds of information about them came in from many different countries. And since the invention of aeroplanes our knowledge of the vast numbers carried by wind has increased yearly. That too is a fascinating subject.

All these regular and spasmodic travels by air have a very important bearing on the distribution of insects throughout the world. They play an important rôle in the population of new lands, and of mixing populations of the same species which may renew the vitality of races. Therefore the underlying principle of all these movements is probably racial because they may improve the physique of a race.

## Dispersal and Migration

So in these days we have given up thinking that the urge which prompts these travellers in the initial stage must be from outside circumstances. On the contrary, it is probably due to some inner urge which we have only just begun to study. It is interesting to find this change of theory because it comes from different directions. Specialists in different groups of insects have independently come to that conclusion, and are more inclined to the belief that there is in such insects a craving for long flights which refuses to be checked until this travel stage has been accomplished. When specialists independently agree on a point concerning their own department of study, that is convincing to outsiders.

The migratory insects which from the beginning have received the most attention are locusts and butterflies. The first because of their tremendous damage to crops, and the second because of their conspicuous appearance, their colour and beauty which makes them universally noticed.

Entomologists were obliged to give up a lot of time to working out the movements of locust swarms. They had to study the different kinds, and their seasons, the dates of their flights, the months when the different species laid eggs, all had to be recorded.

It caused surprise in the middle of the 19th century to find that, when a kite smeared with sticky mixtures was flown among locust swarms, however long the string the kite would be withdrawn covered in locusts. It was a surprise to learn by records at different points of the route that one swarm could travel a very long way; it was a surprise when kite-flying at night proved that these insects still flew on in the dark. But today it is known that the same species may leave Africa and arrive in Russia. And that it can fly at a height of over two miles. By thousands of records in different parts of the globe it has been established at what speed they travel, for how long at a stretch, what they do on arrival. There are maps of the itinerary, time tables and graphs without end, and a special department in the British Museum with a trained staff under the greatest living specialist on locusts, Dr. Uvarov. Records are always being accumulated, migrations are always being dealt with, and various measures are always being used and studied in the field.

Yet, in spite of all this bulk of work concerning locust migrations, and although the insects are being controlled in the various stages, as egg, hoppers and adults, yet still we are no nearer the time when the precise cause of their migration can be clearly understood. Only, it seems clear that the cause is not hunger, competition or scarcity of one sex, but a mysterious inner urge which incites the insects to make these prodigious voyages even for thousands of miles before it is sated.

It is not hunger, because they will leave a land of plenty and may fall in a desert and perish in thousands or may fall into the sea. The urge is not only in the adults, the young wingless larvæ or hoppers may hear that clarion call and start a mass movement in one direction—an astonishing spectacle when the whole surface of the ground seems in motion.

Most mysterious of all is the knowledge now that of one species of locusts in one locality half of them may migrate and the others remain. In one part of the district numbers of them will become restless. They start short circulatory flights returning to their home, this may continue daily for a while. Then suddenly the yearning for flight becomes an uncontrollable passion and the entire locust population—of that district—takes to flight. They may fly at two or three miles above the earth or nearer. They fly with the wind or against it. They fly through storm and fair weather, through various climates, they come down to feed or to rest periodically. But until a certain distance is accomplished, or until they have flown for a certain period, the migration continues. Then by what looks like a general consent it is over. They come to earth, pair, and lay eggs.

Yet all that time the locusts which belong to the same species remain in the district from which their relations departed. This is still unexplained. What can cause the first impulse? Why should it affect one half of the population and not the other?

A most exhaustive comparison of the two forms, the migrants and stay-at-homes, does not reveal a single minute character wherein they differ. Not only their outward appearance but their anatomy gives no clue either. It was thought earlier that some particular organ must be adapted to store extra oxygen for these remarkable migrations but there is no sign of it. There seems no special equipment needed for these amazing feats of endurance.

We may conjecture that an inward change has caused a tropic condition in some of the locusts to which the response is flight. The power which a tropism has to control all the faculties of an insect which is in its grip will be studied in a later chapter, and we shall see that an insect has no volition until the aim is accomplished and the tropism is relaxed. But why some of these locusts become tropic and others are unaffected must be left for future research workers to decide.

Butterfly migration is a very popular subject and most interesting books have been written on it. Several scientists have made a life study of it and published appeals for records of any migrations that came under observation. In this way they collected a mass of information which brought to light very long flights made by certain species of butterflies. They were able to trace the itinerary of the two greatest travellers, the Monarch and the Painted Lady.

The Monarch is widely known, very handsome in tawny and yellow trellis pattern. Its strong wings suggest powers of flight, but the revelations of the distances it can travel were made by meticulous care in connecting locality and date records over numbers of years. There are still a few gaps in this knowledge to be filled. But it is established that there are two distinct races on the American continent, and that while one is moving south from the north the other is moving in a contrary direction. It was established too that the northern race starting in the autumn from the northern states and South Canada reach Florida and California, pass the winter in chosen localities (the same year after year), and in the spring start the return journey laying eggs at intervals on the way north. It has been proved that individual butterflies actually accomplish both flights, which means over two thousand miles. A very startling achievement for a butterfly. The southern race does not travel quite so far.

The movements of other butterflies and some of the moths have been studied as well. There are species with a world-wide distribution. The strong-winged Convolvulus Hawk moth is a sturdy traveller. It has reached almost every country.

It is an impressive sight to witness part of these great migrations, to see butterflies coming inland from the sea in vast numbers but not in close flocks, to watch their arrival and note how furiously hungry they are. I have seen on three separate occasions, in England and on Pacific Islands, masses of wild flowers alive with fluttering butterflies and then in two days' time not a blossom is to be seen because they have all been pollinated and are over. I have seen a long lane of low bushes in the tropics after sunset with every tree a mass of sleeping butterflies with wings folded. Some of the trees at a little distance were a mosaic of black, white and yellow on a background of green. I have watched from a steamer Convolvulus Hawk moths, which were very common on the island I had just quitted, flying in one direction low over the waves at intervals of a quarter of an hour or twenty minutes. Several times I have crossed a line of migration on the sea, once the steamer took the same route and night and day for three days on end we were surrounded by butterflies. Some settled on the rigging directly it was dark, but if one looked upwards as high as could be seen there were butterflies on the wing. Some of the dragonflies have been studied as well but records of their migrations are not so complete.

The urge to travel certainly results in a wider distribution of species and so it may be a natural leaning towards that end. Even caterpillars will walk for long distances before they start making a chrysalis. I remember well how distressing it used to appear when as children we kept caterpillars, they were our choice treasures, we looked upon them with the same affection as our other pets. When at the end of an exciting feeding period a caterpillar would begin its wanderings I used to stand for hours watching until its cravings ceased, feeling that it must be unhappy or discontented with its surroundings. There was something that it missed. It would stop for a moment to examine a twig or leaf, then on with its forced marching. We felt responsible, we imagined there was something we had failed to supply. Then after as much as three hours' walking a Woolly Bear would come to rest at a spot which it had examined and discarded contemptuously a score of times, and suddenly find its ideal resting place and to our vast relief would begin to spin.

Nobody has measured what distance a caterpillar travels in freedom before it pupates. But the urge is very strong and this may be a natural impulse to start the next generation in a new place.

There are myriads of airborne insects which can be carried for very long distances not of their own volition or by their own power but by wind. We have begun to alter our opinion about these flights as well. In earlier days we looked upon those vast numbers which every year are caught up into the upper currents, swept out of forests by gales and cyclones, as victims of forces too strong for them, unwilling travellers. It was taken for granted that few of the delicate insects could survive such rough treatment. For the majority are small light insects, little moths, flies, little beetles and bugs. But among them are winged ants and others with comparatively heavy bodies which we should consider disqualified them for involuntary flight.

But are these accidental migrations of unwilling travellers after all? I have watched moths flying upwards after sundown from one of my camps in New Guinea. When one looked down upon the roof of the forest below, the light-coloured moths could be seen leaving the shelter of foliage and flying upward. Then at a higher altitude on that same mountain, where wind swept with such force over my moth screen that I dared not put down anything without weighting it because it was liable to be whisked away, I have had the screen so covered in insects that they were settling on the top of one another. While they clung to the screen they were safe but those which left it were whirled away into the night helpless to resist.

There must have been thousands that night which came into my limited perimeter, so how many millions were in the air from that part of the forest it is impossible to guess. The wind blew at almost gale force from just after sundown until 2.30 A.M.; all that time insects were being whirled away. Then it dropped, insects that remained in that current must have been deposited else-where.

What instinct made them fly upwards into the wind? We may well ask whether this can be considered accidental or due to a racial urge. Many moths appear to fly upwards to pair; male and female ants are known to have a marriage flight. These could not make long voyages but the wind can be the transporting agent necessary to these races.

So then this type of transport although it appears adventitious may be on a par with migration, a means to an end. I have noticed that some insects at least are not torn from their homes even by cyclones. After an experience when surprised by a cyclone in an uncomfortably high camp on a New Guinea island I found, after it had ceased, insects taking refuge in unwonted positions. Moths, small dragonflies and flies were anchored in crevices under tree roots and rocks, moths were beaten out of thickets in large numbers. For three days after the hurricane I saw no flying insects, but after that their numbers around that camp appeared normal.

This is only one record. We need hundreds of similar experiences before we can formulate any opinion. We need, especially, records of the condition in which an insect arrives after a long flight; research could be carried out on such lines, but needs the right locality and special apparatus.

One very interesting incident makes me believe that delicate insects may survive a rough passage by air more often than we suppose. We are accustomed to consider it a case of survival of the fittest. Insects are often to be seen on board ship, but one cannot consider when we notice them in open sea that they have just come in. They may have been on the ship all the time, they may have emerged from cargo in the hold or from something our fellow travellers brought on board—natives often carry vegetables and roots, or cuttings or small plants in soil, these are usually stowed somewhere on deck and I have caught insects on them.

On this one occasion a very strong gale was blowing and I had the luck to see an insect blown over the rail. I thought it was an insect and when it fell among

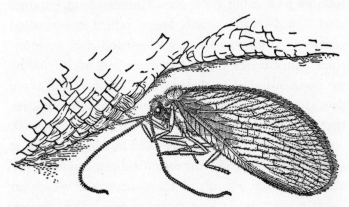

Nerve-winged insect

some copra sacks I crept over to investigate. This had to be done cautiously because of the force of the wind but I located it, got it into a tin and found a sheltered spot where I could examine it.

The ship was at about the centre of Geelvinck Bay in the north of New Guinea, we were at latitude 2° 25′ S. and longitude 125° 4′ E. as I ascertained from the bridge. This meant that we were about 60 miles from the nearest land. Actually a group of atolls, Mios Auri, was 40 miles away, but the wind was not coming from that direction.

## Dispersal and Migration

The insect was one of the nerve-wings, *Hemerobius*, one of the most delicate insects with its gauzy frail wings fine as muslin. Yet here it was, hurled on deck by a wind whose velocity made it necessary for me to hold on to solid objects. And it was not dead. At first sight I thought that it was, but noticed that it was attached to a sack by one claw; I had to disengage it very carefully. This fact and because the limbs were not rigid made me watch it at intervals. After three-quarters of an hour the tip of one antenna was moving; then the rest of it began to move and finally the pair were in motion. After one hour and forty minutes it was standing. If it had been a human being we should consider it had been suffering from shock and had re-covered.

This nerve-wing and another nearly related are seen taking refuge in a strong wind. They carry their wings roof-shaped over the back and are blown sideways or flat if sitting openly on a leaf on a windy day. They are seen flying on still days, but in any breeze I look for them securely anchored under leaves. This voyage I consider definitely accidental not a voluntary yielding itself to the wind, yet it was an advantage to be trans-ported to new ground.

This insect was presumably off its guard but at any rate a 60-mile voyage had not killed it. As we came into port it flew ashore. If such a frail creature can survive we may suppose others have an equal chance but this needs extensive research in different regions. The question of their survival does not concern only their physical condition on arrival although that is very important but we should like to know as well whether they can escape their normal enemies while in a semi-comatose state. If such insects were blown into trees or to the ground in coastal regions patrolled by ants one would suppose that they would have little chance. On high trees, especially inland, they might be given time to recover.

Migrations do not need a strong wind. When small insects take part in one they want only a favourable breeze. Often it is so slight that we hardly detect it, but it serves them. Everybody has seen swarms of aphids suddenly appear in places that have been free of them, the country people call it a blight but it is a migration. They come in clouds, and if not an absolutely still hot day there will be merely a zephyr moving in the air. These do not occur every year. The normal migrations of aphids from one type of food plant to another are started by some change in the insect. But it is only occasionally when a species of aphis happens to be in abnormally large numbers that a mass migration is noticed. It is an event which cannot be passed unmarked when clouds of the insects settle in a garden, the landscape has an altered appearance in a very short time.

It was pests that taught us so much about insect travellers. As might be expected there is great variety in the manner in which insects set about accomplishing the same objective. There is little that can be called monotonous in the insect world. Discoveries about pests and ingenious methods of dealing with them come largely from the United States. Crops are so extensive that pests are on a large scale as well. One of the most interesting discoveries was how the Gypsy Moth migrates. It was introduced into the United States. An introduced species usually does not have its own allotted parasites to keep down numbers so it is liable to run amuck without control.

This was just what the Gypsy Moth did, spreading through forest and committing untold damage on trees. It was certainly spreading and far too quickly. Yet the females cannot fly although strangely enough they have wings, so this was a problem over which entomologists puzzled in vain until a very unexpected and lucky solution was found. It is the caterpillars which fly—that had occurred to nobody until it was observed among other caterpillars and suggested to those who were studying the Gypsy Moth. They have long hairs and when very young the bodies are light enough to be born aloft in a wind, sustained by the hairs. The little caterpillar gets the right position in the wind and lets itself go, when it alights it goes on eating. So the question was answered as to how this pest could be spreading at a rate of five miles a year. Aeroplanes have caught these flying caterpillars at a height of 2,000 feet.

This is not the highest altitude known for airborne insects. The record is 14,000 feet. The traps used by aeroplanes to provide information about those in the air give astonishing results; before these were used it was never even guessed how many kinds of insects took to the air. All sorts of odd insects have been found very high up on mountains, one large dragonfly was seen trapped in a small cave. The wind was blowing it against the side and it could not escape. That record— an early one—helped to fix the idea that insects were so battered if caught by strong winds that they could not survive.

When one species is found widely dispersed across the globe, if it is not a migratory form we are inclined to think that there must be some sort of transport agent which helps to keep up the supply. When the normal means of dispersal are carried out we find that a species which has settled on some distant land if isolated for long will vary either in size, colour or form and so will become a new race.

One species of little wasps puzzled me for years, but I think now that I may have got the solution. They are found on different islands right across the Pacific from the Philippines to Tahiti and they do not vary one jot or tittle. I could not find even a minute difference. If I take the locality label off my series in the Museum I cannot tell which island a specimen came from. Even if insects are closely related one can usually see differences without referring to the labels. But now I think the solution to the problem may be that this particular species can be carried on ships and canoes.

Although they are not conspicuous, being small and black without colour pattern, they are noticed because of their habit of killing little cockroaches and dragging them about. The large cockroaches in ships and houses are so detested by everybody that it is hoped the wasps are killing off young ones. But it is a little silvery cockroach and not the young of the larger species which is the prey, it lives under bark and leaves and is never a nuisance.

My little black wasp is so numerous that whenever I landed afresh on some Pacific island I got into the habit of looking about at once for my friend. She would be there right enough on the beach where I landed, as likely as not she would be dragging a cockroach along by its antennæ or digging a burrow in dry soil or fine sand. It is delightful to watch them engrossed in their task whether hunting or excavating.

Then one day I noticed a Polynesian fisherman packing his belongings into a canoe for a fishing trip across the sea to another island on the horizon. He had fishing gear and food in baskets made of coconut fronds, more fronds were used to cover them from the heat. He had a hearth-stone and logs to make a fire during his trip, and his last act was to collect some sand just on that part of the beach where I had been watching the burial of a cockroach with a wasp's egg on it. I walked down to the canoe and saw him pack the sand under and round his hearth-stone as a safeguard against scorching. Searching the fronds very thoroughly was another wasp of the same species. I saw her triumphantly locate a cockroach and fly to shore with it.

Supposing that wasp had sailed with the canoe and wanted badly to lay an egg she had the wherewithal for her nest on board. And whenever the fishermen scoop up sand for their hearth-stones there is a likelihood of some wasp pupæ being carried off to be thrown out on some other island. So although these wasps do not fly from island to island their eggs or pupæ may be transported by another agency. Conditions would be alike on all these islands and one would not expect to find differences in these wasps' bodily structure. Since very early days large trading canoes have made long trips between island groups and the modern ships are very likely to have sand on board. The little silvery cockroach too is common on all these islands. Their eggs can travel on floating logs without being damaged by sea water, so even the food of the wasps will not vary on different islands.

On a steamer too I have noticed plants being carried by passengers in a kerosene tin that was filled up with sand. There might have been a little family of wasps in it ready to start a colony at the end of their voyage. Here was a grand opportunity for the wasps to take advantage of this means of travelling—and they are equipped for starting life in a new land.

There are other wasp travellers which constantly make use of craft of any description large and small. These are the potter wasps which plaster their little cells of clay all over our bungalows on anything solid or on trees or rocks. There are some species which are common nearly everywhere. I have often met with these on steamers so we can imagine how they are transported. They need a comparatively sheltered spot and a firm foundation. I have seen their little clay vases on steamers built on to the wood-work of cabins, or masts, or even on passengers' luggage on deck.

Their cells are not stocked with cockroaches but with spiders. While a ship is in port a wasp will start building and will be hunting in wharves and warehouses for spiders. When the anchor is raised some little cells will be finished and sealed up with the spiders and eggs inside, others may still be empty. In a little over a fortnight the young wasps begin to hatch out. They don't need food at first until they become active, and by that time the ship may be approaching land. Many times I have watched wasps coming out of a cluster of clay cells while travelling from one island group to another.

Insects' eggs can be transported in logs which float out to sea and are carried immense distances but most eggs cannot survive the soaking in salt water. There are some kinds of beetle grubs which are not affected, however. I have waded out from a beach and chopped up logs that were covered at high tide, and there I found beetle grubs belonging to several different species peacefully feeding inside as though they were on land. Those particular beetles are found everywhere so we can guess one means at least by which they are introduced to new lands. Those trunks had been uprooted, floated down rivers, and the next high tide would carry them out to sea.

There are other bold colonists among small creatures besides the insects. Once when on a schooner and out of sight of land we were making only about two knots when I noticed a floating log with a pair of centipedes on it. They were not having a very comfortable voyage, for the sea was rather rough and every now and then the log turned right over. I thought the centipedes must be washed off. But they can cling firmly with their strong claws and after a minute they would appear on the upper surface of the log again. I often wondered whether that dauntless couple ever reached land in safety.

# 5. Relationship with Plants

IN ANY NUMBER OF DIFFERENT WAYS, SOME we should never dream of, insects and plants are in league to help each other. A very large majority of insects spend most of their lives in waiting on flowers, doing the important fetching and carrying of the precious pollen grains in return for nectar or for some of the pollen. Not all these insects are entirely dependent on flowers for food, most of them have an alternative diet. And some plants are not dependent on insects' visits, they are able to do their own job of fertilizing although cross-fertilization is always an advantage and some insects do it very deftly.

Then there are quite a number of cases—and these are the most interesting of all—where exclusive interdependence has evolved, where flowers are peculiarly adapted to one group of insects only or even to one species. Or we may consider that it is the insects which are peculiarly adapted to the flowers. So exclusive are these partnerships that either side cannot exist without the partner, their lives are so closely interwoven—as we shall see later.

Insects find other uses for plants, they shelter inside flowers against rain or cold or make houses in the structure of trees or plants. In this sort of relationship it is not always evident that the hosts benefit. Little insects may be found sheltering inside the bell-shaped flowers of campanula of various species. They have no business there, they creep inside for a night's lodging or temporary shelter in a storm. But the hairs which grow inside the flower are a safeguard against mischief from unwelcome guests who might visit the nectar and go out without paying. The rightful guests being larger and stronger can push the hairs aside.

Foxglove bells may contain several different kinds of tiny insects; gentians may seem accessible to anyone but the arrangement of hairs in those flowers too form a natural safeguard. It seems to be the general rule that if insects do manage to get to the nectaries they will bring out at least a few pollen grains attached to them somewhere.

But some plants have special outgrowths which are looked upon as adaptations to suit insects, so we must suppose that there is an advantage to be gained by housing them either temporarily or for life. Many have little empty chambers which are taken by ants and these defend their homes and incidentally the plants as well.

Then there is the curious mutual arrangement whereby insects remove sugar wastes, not from blossom but from various parts of plants, stems, or leaves, etc., where they are contained in extra-floral nectaries. Here again are special adaptations which offer direct invitations to insects, for the waste products are exuded in convenient form instead of in a sticky mass which might cause accidents. Sugar in plant tissues is not needed after the period of growth has passed its zenith, it is no longer wanted for building up new tissue. So the plant gets rid of it and eager insects clear it away and lick the surface clean.

This partnership between active insects and stationary plants is charming. Nobody knows for how many millions of years it has been going on. In the very beginning plants were fertilized by simple methods, either self- or cross-fertilized by the aid of wind, water or passing animals, as are some plants still today. But when gay-coloured blossoms began to appear on the earth there was a progressive evolution of more and more complex arrangements of the vital reproductive organs of plants, an enormous variety of different forms which were thrown out in all directions. Side by side with them appeared insects adapted to take an active part in the transport of pollen from flower to flower.

## Insects: Their Secret World

Controversy has raged over which came first. Were insects adapted to flowers or was it the other way round? It is immaterial which appeared first. It suffices to know that these adaptations did evolve and that we can see them all around us in any part of the world today.

Some of the work of pollination can be called casual, but none of it is so impersonal as that which depends on wind or water, animals' fur or feet. The casual scattering of pollen by some insects may be wasteful, and it is interesting to note that the type of flower that allows waste has quantities to dispose of, presumably to allow a margin for what will not reach its objective.

At the other end of the scale where flowers depend on certain insect visitors their mechanism is adapted with exquisite exactitude; the size, weight, shape of body, length of tongue are all considered. And of course habits and sense organs are considered too, for it would be useless for flowers to have special allures such as colour and scent if insects did not possess special sense organs to respond to them. The synchronizing of events is also an important factor. Some flowers only open for a short period so the right kind of insect must have an urge to visit it timed almost to a split second or it might arrive too late.

This is an endless subject. Volumes have been written on it and it is of universal interest. Everybody likes flowers, most people take more than an æsthetic pleasure in them, many have gardens and many live in the country. In any flower bed, in any country lane there are myriads of different devices of flowers adapted to privileged visitors, but unless the mechanism of the flower is understood the fascinating operation is imperfectly followed and there is not so much to marvel at.

A bee can be watched visiting an orchid or a bean flower, a butterfly uncoiling its proboscis to drink nectar, hawk moths in the twilight delicately imbibing while hovering for a few seconds. But in that brief moment when an insect thrusts its head or proboscis into a flower and then withdraws again all sort of things have taken place. That is the part which is marvellous—when the insect by a touch sets the delicate mechanism in motion.

It is easiest to watch the whole operation of pollination taking place on open composite flowers, dandelions, daisies, thistles, sunflowers. The small white or coloured florets are crowded together on one head to attract the attention of insects and so get the operation over quickly and effectively. Scrambling over these flower heads, which give out a delicious scent of nectar from their brimming goblets, are large and small insects. Pollen grains get dusted all over the small ones, and on head and legs of the larger ones, then other flower heads are visited where stigmas are ready to receive them. Not all florets open at the same time; it is interesting to keep watch on one flower head to observe the sequence of florets and to see which are fertilized. On the dandelion for instance they open in succession from the outside ranks inwards until they are all pollinated.

Small beetles will be noticed eating the pollen, cramming it into their mouths. Some of this will be spilt as well, but when they reach the stigmas, after they have been wallowing in the generous supply, enough is left on their bodies to serve the flowers. It is a great advantage to have the florets massed because one insect can pollinate a number of them in a very short time. Although self-pollination can take place, cross-pollination is best completed by the insects passing from flower to flower, and it need not be emphasized that this is more certain than when done by the wind. When, however, the pollen is concentrated into particular organs and confided to a particular insect messenger there is little fear of waste, bar accidents.

Orchids show some of the most astonishing adaptations and they have been exhaustively studied. Pollen instead of being distributed extravagantly is on tiny clubs or flattened racquets and is in such a position in the flower that an insect is bound to touch the sticky disc at the base of the club and carry it off. Wasps and bees may often be caught with the clubs attached to them, in the right position to touch the stigma—which is also sticky—of the next flower. You may watch a bumble bee in Europe bustling into a flower of the Early Purple Orchis and, while it is drilling for nectar in the tissue of the spur at the back of the flower, a pair of little

Bumble bee pollinating the Spotted Orchid

Bumble bee pollinating the Spotted Orchid

yellow clubs of pollen being arranged on its head. If you catch it when it has finished drinking you will find them fastened on the velvet of its forehead. Now, if the clubs remained in that same position when the bee visited another flower nothing would happen. The pollen would not reach the sticky stigma at the back of the group of organs for the clubs would only collide with them. But their nature is such that the moment the bees bring them into contact with the outside air they begin to flag, and they flag forward until they have collapsed into a horizontal position. They are then at the exact angle required, and the bee in its anxiety to reach nectar in the next flower will force them forward until they touch the sticky surface of the stigma which relieves them of their load. An essential point is that the sticky disc at the base of the pollen clubs should be at exactly the right angle. The weight of the bee is of importance here, for as it alights on the lower petal, the lip of the orchid, its weight depresses it and lowers the disc by the fraction of a millimetre so that the insect's forehead presses into it. The position of the bee's hind legs in the illustration shows this.

The amount of force that an insect can use has much to do with setting the mechanism in motion, for this reason it is surprising to notice that some orchids are served by little bees as well as big ones. But little bees are very persistent and quite strong. The pollen club will not be on the head and perhaps only one will be dislodged instead of a pair. Very often it will lodge on the stiff bristles of either the side or the undersurface of the little bees, but in that position it will brush against the stigma of the next flower as readily as it did on the bigger bee's forehead.

The pushing power of a small bee is remarkable, it seems not to be commensurate with its size. When I am collecting the tiny species I have to see that the stitching of my fine meshed bee-net is quite close and regular. A space between two stitches will be discovered by the bee, and then I have to hunt carefully for my specimen which has pushed itself inside the hem whence it is very difficult to dislodge it without damage. So I am never surprised when a tiny bee disappears into a flower and comes out with a heavy club of pollen.

For exclusive visitors of only one size every row of hairs and every ridge in an orchid's throat has a meaning, they are to guide a bee's tongue or a moth's proboscis so that they cannot err. Systems such as this prevent the wrong type of visitor from entering and putting the exquisite mechanism out of gear. It must not be imagined that there are never any failures. It is often found that a whole colony of orchids have produced only a few seeds. However even a few seeds can carry on the race.

In all probability accidental misses or clumsiness in the operation cause most inconvenience to the insect. One feels desperately sorry for some insects that cannot get rid of some part of the apparatus but must drag it about with them until the end of their lives. Moths are found blinded by discs clamped on to their eyes, and beetles with discs plastered on the palps of the mouths glueing their jaws together.

Charles Darwin, who made such an exhaustive study of orchids' pollination by insects, noticed a tiny beetle which had been overweighted by a pollen club larger than itself and had succumbed. He remarked in his book that the beetle had been punished for undertaking a task beyond its strength. A very severe sentence on the unfortunate victim and considered only from the orchid's viewpoint! From the beetle's viewpoint the orchid had ill-used a willing servant by not safeguarding it against being caught in very dangerous machinery.

We are accustomed to look on flowers as gentle and frail but some of their manœuvres to make insects slave for them are brutal. Some will squirt drops of viscous fluid at them directly they pass inside, to which they fasten pollen grains while it is moist, and the remainder clots their plumy hairs together. That to a smart little bee that always combs itself so carefully must be very distressing. And whatever may be in store in the way of violent treatment, the insect directly it has given in to the enticement must go through with it.

It is difficult to understand why some flowers, especially the larger orchids, secrete fluids in specially evolved pouches. One specimen was found to carry an ounce of this fluid. Bees are found with their wings drenched crawling out of these orchids. What the flower gains thereby is not evident unless bee visitors are to be warned off. Any insect with a retentive memory would not be expected to make a second trial if suddenly pitched into a bath after crawling through a tunnel. An unpleasant experience should make it avoid similar flowers, but that depends upon the power of the allure. It might be even more risky for small insects for they might be drowned outright yet on the other hand they might be able to crawl above the brink of the fluid.

Such a savage reception for visitors would not be surprising if practised by insectivorous plants. These are the sinister—though very interesting—groups of plants which lure, trick and trap luckless insects, drowning or suffocating them in order to absorb their life juices. This is indeed a one-sided association. The insect gets no compensation from these deadly enemies.

There are some very ingenious flower traps to hold insects prisoner until they have finished the job of pollination exactly in the prescribed manner. Living insects are required for this—it is not part of the scheme to kill them, they may be kept for an hour or two or even for several days. Sometimes they are required to panic, then sufficient space is allowed for them to use their wings and they fly about and dust themselves thoroughly with pollen, which they place in position on stamens either of the same flower or of another. Many a time when a flower is opened we find insect corpses inside. This does not mean that they are insectivorous plants but that the insects have not set in motion the proper apparatus which will open the trap.

What is so remarkable about all these special designs is that parts of the plant have been modified to an extraordinary degree in order to adapt them for some abnormal function. And the number of different devices is astonishing. In one genus every species may have a different mechanism and be served by different kinds of insects.

Charles Darwin made such thorough investigation of orchids' mechanism that by examining any he could realize the size and structure of the insects needed to pollinate it. One day he was faced with a totally new arrangement and was puzzled. He pondered for some time, then guessed how it worked, so he touched it with a hair in the way he imagined the appropriate type of insect would do. To his delight the flower responded, he had guessed correctly. He was so gratified that it is mentioned in his book though with his habitual modesty.

Another renowned research worker, the New Zealand botanist Cheeseman, had a similar triumph. He examined an orchid of a type unfamiliar to him and concluded that an insect of a certain size could work the mechanism. So he selected a beetle which he considered suitable and made it walk into the entrance of the flower. After 20 minutes the beetle walked out again with a little pollen club on its head.

No public demonstration from one's fellow creatures could give such a satisfying tribute to one's sagacity!

Not all orchids associated with insects have bright colours. Some are green or brown and are very inconspicuous when they grow among low plants and grasses. In a mountainous region of Papua, where I encamped at 9,000 feet, was a little colony of very peculiar orchids which it would have been a great pity to miss. I nearly missed them because they were growing in a shallow damp depression among reeds and grasses. One blossom caught my eye not because of the color which was a dull beige with pink veins but because of two long slender spikes that I took for grasshoppers' antennæ. Then I stooped down and recognized them as green-hood orchids which trap insects. They are not insectivorous being benevolently inclined towards the insect world, but their treatment of visitors is so strange that the device for caging them must be described in detail.

The upper middle sepal and petals combine in a hood to shelter and hide the column, which is bent back at the base so that it lies close to the upper sepal and is partly joined to it. The side sepals are united for half their length so that they form an upright fork. It was the fine tips of these which I had taken for an insect's antennæ.

The hooded column rests between these supports.

So the whole flower appears to be upside-down compared with the normal arrangement to which we are
accustomed. It looks too as if it is in bud because
the flower does not open fully. Its work of pollination
is carried out very secretly and privately inside.

The lip of the orchid—usually the lower landing place
—is above. In the bent-over position the lip which is
very slender protrudes between the forks at their base.
It is not where we should look for it but is where an
insect would naturally alight because it is at the only
entrance to the flower. On the lip is something which
looks like a tiny fringed cushion, this is of a different
shape in each species. It is extremely irritable, even a
fungus midge or tiny beetle causes it to spring inwards
carrying the insect with it and closing the trap still farther.

Now the insect finds itself at the bottom and proceeds to make its way upwards. It is lighter at the top
where tips of sepals and petals are folded; no doubt that
is why it crawls upwards towards the light and the
only means is by climbing the column. There is not
much space even for a tiny insect, it has to push its
way upwards and in doing so is smeared with viscid
fluid secreted in the tissue of the column. At the top
it must brush against the pollen and this gets attached
to it. Now the whole of this strange performance takes
place in another flower. Apparently no wages are paid
for it but the insect may find a little sweet secretion in

the tissue at the bottom of the flower—let us hope that it has at least that compensation.

I watched those plants on Mt. Tafa very closely but though several times there were tiny beetles flying near I never saw one settle on a green-hood. This may have been too late in the season for the species which normally pollinates it, for there were seeds in the dead heads and little plants were coming up in numbers from the soil.

It can be seen that this is an extreme example of modification and special adaptations. No large insect could force its way in and there would be nothing to attract it. The small visitors in spite of rather rough shocks at the entrance carry out a more dignified procedure than in some flowers, and they are noticed to leave in about half an hour, which is better than being detained for days.

Some of the arum lilies give an example of a long-term imprisonment. It is the act of pollination which starts off the mechanism for release, but insects do not always proceed progressively and if there is any check the trap won't open. The common wild arum (lords and ladies) of Europe is one of these. There are no nectaries but the flower has a fœtid smell which attracts certain small insects. This may be all they get out of it unless there is some secretion in the tissue which they can tap. One advantage is warmth. It has been found that the temperature inside the sheath is 10 degrees higher than outside. They enter the sheath without obstruction but following the scent walk down the spathe in the centre, to do this they have to pass by two circles of stiff hairs which grow downwards. Small insects can pass by pressing against the more flexible tips but they are unable to get back again for the tips only bend one way. The insects are then in a little chamber among the pollen and as they panic trying to find a way out it is dusted on to them. As the upper barrier cannot be passed they must go downwards through the second zone of hairs which is arranged on the same principle. In the lower chamber are the stigmas. Now comes the delightful part of this trap, for when sufficient pollen has been scattered to fertilize the flower this act causes the zones of hairs to slacken, contract and finally shrivel. So there is nothing to impede the visitors from returning to a free life once more.

It may take two or three days to effect their release because a little spasmodic pollination is not enough to open the trap, it must be distributed lavishly.

Quite as tricky as orchids' mechanisms are those of the large family *Asclepiadaceæ*, and among these too there is an astounding number of different devices. Most of these plants are climbers, the beautiful waxy-flowered Hoya and the curious Dutchman's Pipe are well known.

Entomologists quite often find that specimens of wasps and bees have chains of small black discs entangled on their legs. Some of the discs may still support a pair of spoon-shaped membranes to which pollen has been attached. They belong to some species of *Asclepias*. There are little pockets in the flowers kept well filled from the nectaries, but a large insect in order to reach them has to straddle the reproductive organs. Between the anthers are curious slits shaped like the letter "Y." The insect gets its foot into the wide farther part of the slit when it settles on the flower and after drinking, in the act of withdrawing it, pulls the foot backwards into the narrow end—the stem of the "Y"— and therefore has to make an effort to free it. This jerk does the trick, for the foot presses against a sticky disc and pulls out a pair of spoons on which the plant has already loaded pollen.

When the insect settles on another flower the spoons, which have deflexed into the correct position, are pushed well inside to the sticky stigmatic surface at the back while the visitor is reaching for the honey jars. It is all exquisitely timed and even the measurement of the insect's foot has been taken. It is an example of a very complex series of adaptations only found in a few species and they vary slightly among themselves. The operation can be watched on *Asclepias cornuti* in gardens.

It may be judged by the numbers of discs collected on insects' legs, particularly on those of wasps, that there is a strong inducement to carry out this tricky business. The stout little honey pots provide an explanation.

Wasps have **very** keen appetites because of their energetic labours; one notices them being quite rough with flowers in some moods in their anxiety to get at nectar quickly after exhausting themselves over some exacting job.

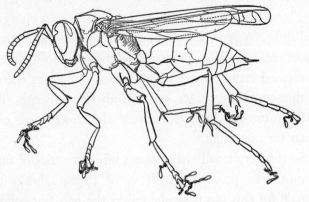

Wasp's legs encumbered by chains of pollen club discs

In the illustration there are 27 discs stuck together in chains. I noticed this wasp which I took in New Guinea savagely biting at something which I thought must be a captured prey. When I found the festoons of discs it struck me what a real hindrance they must be to a busy insect with pressing social duties. When one considers what numbers of insects there must be in a similar unhappy condition which never come to our notice, one feels that these strange flowers deal very unfairly with their friends by obliging them to go through a fully occupied life with discarded paper bags stuck to their limbs.

Of those cases where one partner would cease to exist if the other were exterminated the *Pronuba* moth and the *Yucca* plants is one of the most beautiful. They belong to the aloes, sometimes called Adam's Needle and have handsome, cream, bell-shaped flowers on a central spike. When the flowers open they give out a strong sweet scent at night, a message to the tiny moth with its burnished cream wings which comes out of its cocoon at the same time, mates, and is ready to lay its eggs. The dates must synchronize because the flowers are only open for one night.

So the very small visitor starts off on a series of most unmoth-like proceedings. It is of course always the female for this business; she enters the bell and collects pollen, which she rolls into a ball and tucks below her proboscis under a pair of specially formed palps. Then she flies with this load to another flower, pierces the wall of the empty ovary with her long ovipositor and lays her eggs inside. After this she climbs to the top of the pistil and crams the pollen into it, thus making sure that her offspring will have seeds to feed upon.

Consider all the adaptations for this operation! It is quite exceptional for a moth to collect pollen in the first place. The palps which hold the ball are very large and have a double row of spines on the inner side which hold it in position. No other moths have such palps.

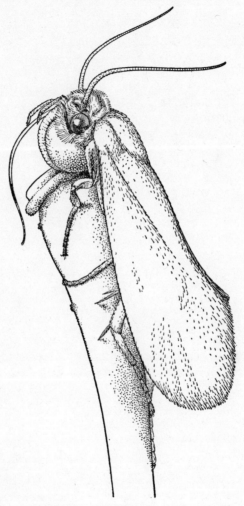

Pronuba moth pushing pollen into the pistil of Yucca

## Relationship with Plants

And the ball is usually about three times as big as the moth's head. The series of instinctive actions are marvellous following one another with clockwork precision. The mechanism of the flower is perfectly adapted and without *Pronuba* pollination could not possibly be carried out. The scent too, though strong, does not attract other insects to make futile experiments with what does not concern them.

If the caterpillars when they hatched devoured all the seeds there would be no advantage to the *Yucca*. But the liberal ration of pollen which the *Pronuba* rams down the style produces so many seeds that some always remain when the caterpillars have finished feeding. Out of 200 ovules about 20 are enough.

Crevices of bark, hollows and in fact anything which offers shade or shelter from cold and damp are very convenient for small insects such as earwigs, beetles, cockroaches and crickets. But the social insects, particularly ants, make homes for rearing their broods. Particularly ants because certain species have become adapted to certain trees, bushes or plants and are not found elsewhere.

This is a subject that has been dealt with from both sides, the botanical and the entomological. It is taken for granted that plants indispensable to one kind of insects must be equally dependent on their lodgers, but though such arguments are intriguing they cannot prove this point in every case. Except in a few cases all the advantages seem to be on the insects' side.

Certain swellings, nodes, protuberances in which ants choose to reside used to be quoted as adaptations put out by the plant, but many of these turn out to be abnormalities, principally the work of gall-makers—sap has been diverted and tissue distorted by minute creatures. These, when they have finished their life cycle, creep out through a tiny exit hole. Ants soon discover an uninhabited shelter probably hollowed out by the last tenants and they take possession. A queen occupies it and lays eggs, or a batch is carried in from the nearest nurseries after the place has been thoroughly tidied, then a new ants' nest is started.

Trees in the tropics are usually full of different kinds of ants—some vegetarians and some carnivorous. Such trees will not be defoliated by caterpillars because ant workers are making an hourly search for food and will discover them. But as ants have a habit of protecting aphids and any of their relatives which give out sweet secretions when milked, it cannot be said that all enemies of the tree are kept away, on the contrary sap-drinking insects are encouraged.

One very striking advantage of a real benefit to the host has been noticed among orchids of an epiphytic nature which grow in cracks of bark. Certain ants choose the fine roots for their nests. They bring up soil and pile it rather loosely among the roots, then form little corridors through this soil along the growing roots. These are good airy conditions which will keep the nest healthy. It is found that during the dry season a lot of the little orchids dry up completely and die in exposed positions on the trunks, but all those which have been built in with soil by ants survive. So there we have a picture of mutual accommodation which can be plainly seen, in other cases benefits may be mutual but direct evidence is lacking.

Among curious partnerships is that between an acacia of Central America, the Bull's Horn Thorn, and ants. The tree has soft green foliage and very long sharp thorns. Some of them are hollow and inhabited by very aggressive ants which rush out and defend it with zest if the branches are touched. Everybody who lives in such districts avoids those trees, but human beings are not their natural enemies. It is true that beasts are deterred from browsing on the foliage but in any case the long thorns would be sufficient protection. Much more destructive enemies than beasts are leaf-cutting ants which strip any soft-leaved trees to make mould for their mushroom beds. From these leaf-cutting ants the aggressive ants nesting in the tree are a sure protection, and it is interesting to see the trees with their fresh green foliage untouched in a locality where every available tree has been denuded.

It used to be thought that the ants cleared out the tissue from thorns before taking up their abode, but apparently something feeds there first and leaves an exit hole which ants would not be able to drill for themselves in the hard cover of mature thorns.

In addition to providing homes these acacias put out tiny green sausages on the tips of their leaves which appear to be adaptations to suit the Bull's Horn Thorn ants, they certainly are an immense advantage to them. In the Panama Zone I have watched ants on these trees running in an out of their thorns, drinking from extra-floral nectaries and fetching green sausages for the broods. The trees seem to give ideal conditions to resident ants, any duties are well paid for by such luxuries denied to many of their hard-working neighbours.

Another type of vegetable growth very convenient for ants is the aerial tuber roots of some climbing plants, epiphytes, which are usually at a considerable distance from the ground tangled up with other aerial roots, stems and branches in the dense network of tropical forests. The tubers selected by ants are full of holes like a sponge and so provide ready-made passages. Some remain soft and fibrous, others get tough as they mature.

For ants they are ideal homes because the passages open into wider chambers excellent for broody queens or for segregating eggs and larvæ of different ages. You will seldom find one of these tubers uninhabited and there are several different species of ants which gladly appropriate them. Ants are found actually to start these epiphytes growing in chosen sites by carrying seeds.

The same origin produces what are known as ants' gardens. Ants carry up embryo tubers and place them in a spot favourable to their plans, in bark or lodged in the crook of a bough; they bring up soil too and vegetable detritus to add to it. In a short time the vegetable world is making full use of this foundation. Other epiphytes strike and send upward growths into the branches and long dangling roots to the ground. Creepers take off from it to the nearest trees to twine round limbs. Little ferns appear, mosses, lichens and orchids. In one garden as many as 10 different species have been counted. They are very conspicuous, these ants' gardens, and may be very numerous being quite a feature of the landscape in some districts. And for ants the advantages are obvious, their nests are in the fibrous masses of roots and their workers have trails all over the upper parts of trees which form the roof of the forest.

The oddest association of all—in this case it cannot be called a partnership—is between an Australian orchid and an ichneumon. The very surprising details were published by an Australian botanist Edith Coleman after she and her daughter had watched near Melbourne on several days the Small Tongued Orchid being pollinated.

It was her daughter who first noticed what happened.

She called her mother's attention to the fact that these insects were going *backwards* into the flowers, which seemed very unwonted behaviour. Then they both watched and found that it was a normal proceeding. The male ichneumons were the only insects seen visiting the flowers and they always entered backwards. Or rather, they sat on the flower with their back to the entrance, their forelegs on the lip which makes an accommodating landing place, and then forced the tip of the body backwards inside the opening.

Having discussed the matter with botanist friends and entomologists it was found that nobody had ever heard of anything like it. Everybody was naturally very stirred over the phenomenon. So the Colemans sought out a locality where numbers of Small Tongued Orchids were growing and made a thorough and prolonged investigation observing as closely as possible exactly what did take place.

It is no unusual sight to see ichneumons of all kinds or any other parasitic insects on blossoms. Some groups look for caterpillars or other larvæ to lay their eggs upon. Any of them may alight just for a snack of nectar if it can be reached easily. But though these plants were minutely examined with a lens there was no sign of larvæ and the nectar of the orchids certainly could only be reached by expert insects. Besides, for either of these actions an insect will not deliberately turn its back on the flower and put its head in the air as these *Lissopimpla*

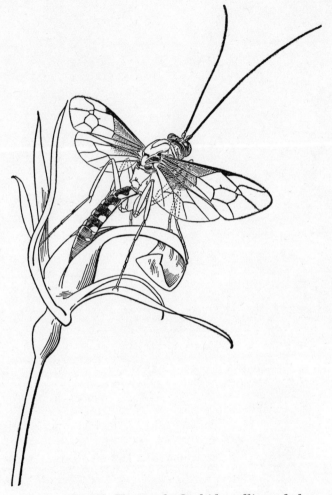

Australian Small Tongued Orchid pollinated by an
ichneumon

were doing and then fly off without examining any other part of the plant.

It was on hot days with a breeze that the insect visitors arrived. There is a scent from the orchids faint to human perception but in all probability it is much stronger to these insects. Mrs. Coleman thought they were guided by sight as well for they always flew down from the trees, finding the flowers without difficulty, so some other sense was certainly the first directive.

Having backed into the opening of the flower, the insect bent the extreme tip of its very flexible body into the precise position for the upper surface of the last and the penultimate segments to rest on the orchid's prominent rostellum with its dark sticky disc. The insect would quiver for a moment and then remain motionless.

After a second or two it began to free itself. This required quite a strong effort; the flower could be seen shaking while it disengaged its organs. If the Colemans took the insect by the wings it could be plainly felt that the flower was resisting, indicating a very tight fit. When the insect had pulled its body out through the opening they would see a club of pollen fixed by its disc on to the tip of the body—never on any other part. Part of the pollen was sometimes shed on the same flower but the bulk was carried to the next. If nothing disturbed the insect the result was always successful.

We search in vain for mutual advantages in this astounding business, not even a niggardly sip of nectar is yielded but the flower gets a very delicate operation performed by a specialist. The only explanation that is forthcoming is that the *Lissopimpla,* which were males in every case observed, seek out the flowers under the impression that they are mating and carry out a mock copulation. If we accept this we must suppose that the orchid's scent resembles that of a female of the same species, which together with the mimicry of female productive organs gives a perfect deception to the ardent suitor.

I have often taken insects belonging to that genus of handsome insects in their black glossy suits ornamented with white, and have never perceived any scent at all from the females though that of allied groups is very strong and frequently disagreeable. The adaptations of this particular orchid towards this objective seem to be unique. It is always possible that other flowers may function similarly, playing similar tricks on insects but so far they have not been observed.

# 6. Parasites and Predators

THERE IS SOMETHING VERY REPUGNANT TO us about parasites—beings that live on other beings' capital, either on reserve stores accumulated by their labours or worse still on their bodily reserves. It is because we claim a right to what we earn by our own faculties, mental or physical. We may covertly admire human parasites that can exploit their fellows with least expenditure to themselves, but we seldom express admiration openly because popular opinion does not really condone human exploitation of human beings in any form.

Parasitism seems to be a natural development but leads into a blind alley. On consideration we admit that nearly every form of life lives on destruction of other forms, but that is not true parasitism. The true parasite depends entirely upon a host. And it is decadent, it is on the downward trend while its host may be on the upward. For if the parasite should become extinct the host is not impeded thereby but if the host should become extinct the parasite must perish.

As may be expected, insects which in one form or another tap all the world's resources have evolved very efficient parasitic types to exploit their fellows. There are various grades; we can trace parasitism step by step. It is a sad tale. It starts with partial parasitism, parasitic habits in the growing stage only, and we follow it to the lowest dregs of degradation, where the beautiful being which we call an insect has become a disgusting inert sack consisting only of digestive machinery and embryonic reproductive organs. Yet these are perfect parasites, that is to say their vital energy is concentrated on parasitism alone. For to be perfectly equipped for the rôle means the gradual abortion of functions, and then the loss of organs through disuse until only a bag of juices with a mouth is left, like maggots but still more inert. As such parasites can never regain their lost limbs and faculties it is considered that they are on the road to extinction.

Parasitism is worth studying. Among insects every phase, partial and entire, may be found, and finally social parasitism practised by some races of the social insects. These last illustrate slave-making in its most vicious form, the exploitation by aggressive races of gentle, timid races.

It is among ants that we find this and scientists are of the opinion that it is an abnormal development which will bring its own punishment of extinction. For there are some races which cannot live without slaves to feed them and wait on them. Such ant races may have been more numerous in the past. There are few remaining today, and those too must sooner or later pay the penalty for flouting the universal law of strenuous competition by which progressive racial development is assured.

It is a curious illustration which should give us pause.

The females of some parasites are highly specialized forms very different from their larvæ. They are lithe and active with a high-grade nervous system and of exquisite structure. It is interesting to watch them with vibrating wings and quivering antennæ locating those insects on which the next generation will feed. Many parasitize the wood-boring beetles and can be seen walking about on tree trunks to find the most convenient spot to insert the instrument for placing the eggs. This is a most exacting operation and the instrument, the ovipositor, is extremely delicate. It is a fine tube, some are no thicker than a horsehair, protected by a sheath with a sharp point at the tip. This has to be driven into bark by separating the bundles of fibre until there is a free passage for the eggs which pass down the tube.

Inside the timber are grubs living in cells which they

have eaten out of the wood. Eggs which produced these grubs were laid by the same method, placed by the ovipositors of their mothers. There are no holes left in the bark to indicate where these cells may be. The female parasites obtain that information through their sense organs.

There is a beautiful parasite, *Rhyssa*, with a very long ovipositor which it drives through timber straight into cells of a large sawfly borer. This is a wonderful feat and for those who may have the chance of watching it from outside it is a truly absorbing sight. The *Rhyssa* may spend an hour in locating grubs, walking over the same spot, touching it with the tips of her antennæ curved downwards. Whether she hears the vibration of jaws where grubs are feeding or is using some other sense cannot be guessed. In any case it is successful. The instrument has to be very long yet slender for piercing the wood. And it must reach inside a cell because the *Rhyssa* grubs are helpless, legless bags with beaks, efficient for wriggling and for attaching themselves to the sawfly grubs and living upon them. They will avoid destroying the vital organs of the host until they have advanced their own development to the point where they must pupate. Then they will consume everything and leave only the host's shrivelled skin.

When the female *Rhyssa* has decided upon the exact point to pierce so that the egg will be landed safely inside a cell, the long instrument is coiled slightly at the base so that with the long hind legs braced the tip is brought to the bark. Then begins the patient work to and fro till the greater part of the tube is inside and an egg can safely be sent down it. The sheath which is in two parts dovetailed together, curves back as the tube is inserted. It is fully as difficult to extricate the ovipositor when all is safely finished. It may break, especially if the *Rhyssa* is disturbed.

So the senses of the female parasites need to be complex to carry out their work while all the larvæ need are reflex actions.

Even the aquatic insects do not escape from parasites which have evolved special equipment to follow them under water. Caddisworms might be thought immune against attack as they live inside tough little cases ornamented with local objects, pebbles, grit and leaves which form admirable camouflage. But their parasites follow and discover them, for females are able to breathe under water until they have finished placing the eggs. They do this by various methods. Some of them creep down the stems of plants where there are minute air bubbles caught in hairs, some are able to carry enough air in their system until the return to upper regions, but each species has the necessary equipment.

So all through the various orders parasitic forms keep down the numbers of each race. There would be little chance of survival in many of these persecuted races if it were not for the large number of the progeny. This

allows some fortunate ones to escape from insect parasites and predators as well as their other enemies.

When we notice enormous batches of eggs laid by
some insects this is no assurance that the same number
of insects will reach maturity. Far from it, perhaps only
one survivor or a couple will remain to carry on the next
generation. It is only when something has hindered
the development of parasites in one season that we can
realize the great numbers that can be produced when
controls are lifted.

There are special parasites for all the different stages—
eggs, larval, pupal and mature. Some insects have two
generations but their parasites may also evolve that same
habit. Thus the eggs are attacked and those that escape
unscathed and hatch out larvæ are still in danger from
the second brood of the same parasite, which attacks
larvæ. Even when they have finished the pupal stage
they may be full of parasites. It is a race for the female
parasitized insects to pair and to lay eggs before the
internal organs are devoured, yet these species do survive
in spite of all.

It can be imagined how the parasitic races of ants
began, first by marauding raids, then by capturing live
prisoners which were given the menial work of the nests,
and finally the races evolved that are helpless without
slaves. All these different phases exist today.

Slave raids are carried out by many different races
of ants as part of their normal work. An excellent first-

hand account of one of these shows that there can be a stiff resistance put up by the ants which are attacked, they do not meekly allow their progeny to be kidnapped. It is the larvæ and pupæ which are stolen. In this account of a battle the attackers were black and the defenders red which gave a fair opportunity to watch what was happening. The battle raged for four or five hours before the blacks finally penetrated the well-defended nurseries which were very large. When at last the struggle was over the conquerors were occupied for nearly two days in carrying off larvæ and pupæ to their own nest.

Livingstone witnessed another battle in Africa, the raiders also were black and attacked a red race. All his sympathy was with the victims who fought stoutly in a losing battle. And while all was being done to keep the invaders from the nurseries, some of the workers were scattering in all directions each carrying in her mouth either a larva or pupa. "No living creature shows greater courage or greater fury in battle!" Livingstone wrote.

The normal finish to such engagements is that the defenders are outnumbered. A very strong nest of raiders will turn out in full force and as fast as they fall others fill the gap but there are many casualties on both sides. One very savage battle was watched between two colonies of black tree ants of the same species. There were such huge numbers of dead on the ground afterwards that 5 litre measures were filled with them. It was reckoned there must have been 40,000 corpses. That signified a very large community which had been attacked, therefore a large number of slaves in the form of pupæ must have been carried to the victor's nurseries but arranged in heaps distinct from their own progeny.

There is an interesting record of an internecine warfare which was kept up all spring and summer. By late autumn one colony was completely wiped out and the young were duly transported without one worker to defend them. The cause is usually territory, on that occasion it seems to have been a tree heavily infested with aphids which gave promise of large herds of milch cows for the victor.

An occasional slave raid does not appear to react unfavourably on a community, or lessen their racial vitality, rather the reverse. What is an undoubted evil leading to the deterioration of physical powers is that habit of depending on slaves which is practised by comparatively few ant races. The best-known are the amazon ants and sword ants. The pernicious habit has been tolerated for so long that these ants cannot exist without slaves which treat them as they would their own larvæ, feeding them with predigested food from their own crops. The slave owners do no work, they join in no sort of homely, domestic work. The only occasions when they exert themselves at all is when they march out of the nest in great crowds to take possession of other ants' nests. There are certain species which are habitually raided.

So dependent are these ants on their slaves that when attempts were made to keep them in artificial nests for observation they always died in a few days of starvation if not supplied with slaves. Even the most tempting food if put near them awoke no response for they literally could not feed themselves.

Before it was known that the larvæ of slave races were brought up in the slave owners' nurseries, scientists were very puzzled to know what strange ants were doing in the nests of other species. They certainly were not of the same race yet seemed quite at home and were never molested as strangers would be. Then the life history was carefully traced bit by bit.

There are legions of predators among insects which hunt them day and night. Carnivorous beetles, crickets, assassin flies, dragonflies, the nerve-winged group, a large number of bugs and many others. Among them are some that are remarkable, perhaps some of the most interesting are praying mantis and certain of the bugs.

The praying mantis belongs to the grasshopper order. But instead of the broad muscular hind legs for leaping, the fore pair have become specialized limbs for trapping their prey. They are very elegant traps with a double row of spines like teeth of a saw which fold against the other joint of the leg with similar spines, so that the two sides have a grip from which few insects ever escape.

To judge the strength of these mantids one only needs to see them with a large struggling bee or wasp trying to free itself and to sting its captor. With its slender legs clutching twigs or plants the mantis's opaque eyes gaze into space and it remains immovable until its victim is exhausted. The mantis's method of striking down on a flying insect and holding it with both forearms prevents its stinging. In all the captures that I have watched I have never seen one get a sting.

Bees seem a favourite prey. Mantids will always drop what they are eating if they hear a humming. Their patience is inexhaustible for they wait for the victim to come near instead of hunting it. Some which I kept in a cage would invariably choose the lighter end, take a strategic position and remain immovable until the most favourable moment for striking. If I turned the cage they would make their way to the other end guided by the same instinct that causes their prey to stay nearest to the light.

Some bug predators too show definite preference for bees. There is one kind that I found in New Guinea which has a very simple but most effective mode of camouflage. They exude a sticky secretion and so become covered in the debris of their immediate neighbourhood; grass seeds, pollen, petals cling to them, so they are lost in their background. Besides this they take up a curious attitude which makes deception complete.

When free of disguises the bug is very distinguished

Predator bug spearing a small bee

in brown velvet corsage with pants to match. Under a lens the velvet appears as long hair, but it is not ordinary hair, each hair is a hollow tube connected with a gland which exudes the viscid fluid. Glistening drops on the tips of the hairs can be seen with the naked eye.

When the bug takes up its peculiar watching attitude the forelegs with their velvet patches are drawn up so that they fit close together in front against the waist-coat, forming a velvet screen. It is not unlike a blossom though there is no definite mimicry. The essential point is that it is un-buglike, and can sit in an exposed position on flowering shrubs or plants without being in the least conspicuous.

It was a great advantage to keep the living bugs under observation to watch the attitude they take while waiting for prey and when they strike. The whole insect seems to suddenly fall to pieces and out of the middle shoots the ugly head with its long proboscis which pins the prey and sucks it dry. They have an enormous appetite, I never knew them refuse food.

The praying mantis on the other hand has periods of rest. When the female is ready to form her nest is the time when it seems impossible to sate her. This is excusable when it is remembered that all the material for a nest five times the bulk of her body comes out of it. This is the occasion for a domestic tragedy if the male should unfortunately be too handy. It is all grist for the mill and furthers the sole objective which is to make suitable preparations for the next generation.

A Dutch naturalist discovered that one species of the predatory bugs appears to dope ants which are its principal victims. Instead of viscous fluid the bugs have a sweet secretion, but there must be some other ingredient because of the disastrous effect which it has upon ants. The bug takes up a position on one of the busy ant highways and when an ant is near raises the front part of the body. This exposes tufts of hair which probably send in the ant's direction a whiff of scent that is like that of aphid sugar. The ant runs up to the bug and eagerly sips the drops on the hair tips. Then in a few moments there are symptoms of poisoning, an attack of partial paralysis, the victim curls itself and draws up its legs. This is the moment for the bug to strike, pin it with the proboscis and suck it dry.

It is a very curious performance. One guesses that the ants might be too active if not doped. Certainly if intended victims escaped there would be a chance of their learning to avoid this enemy. The nature of the dope is not known. It is a very effective weapon and the bug need never exert itself.

Bees too may be intoxicated by certain secretions as is well known, and no instincts seem to warn them of their limitations. Darwin had a truly delightful story of a bumble bee. Somebody had a Guatemalan orchid in his greenhouse in bloom which a bumble bee visited spending some time imbibing the nectar. She emerged and searched for another flower but being unsuccessful returned to the same one for another sip. This alas was her undoing, she came out staggering, fell on her back and remained so for some time. Later however she did recover and flew away. Darwin commented that the nectar was evidently of too strong a vintage for the heads of British bees.

# 7. Pests

EVEN PEOPLE ONE WOULD CALL INTELLI-
gent often say of insects which happen to need a share
of this world's products, "What's the good of those insects? Why don't we exterminate them?" Or, as somebody said to me recently, "I can't think how anybody
can be interested in insects, I think them revolting
little creatures."

Such an illiberal attitude towards the universe if accepted literally! But nobody can seriously imagine that
everything in the world exists to serve the human race.
As for the person quoted, one would like to know what
insects would say of him if they could criticize. Perhaps
they would think him a revolting great creature. And
what opinion could a wasp express of those who grudge
a little sip of jam in return for keeping the garden clear

of injurious grubs for the whole of the summer? It is shameful that even insects which do work for us are squashed when they come to claim their modest salary.

It must be allowed of course that insects are quite brazen robbers, profiteers and opportunists. They exploit everything, nothing is safe from their ravages. That is why there are such myriads of different types, because each has adaptations for exploiting. All their habits, instincts and tools and instruments of their own bodies are evolved for that one objective.

Where insect races clash with the human race is by attacking what we need ourselves, our food, clothing, crops, flower gardens, seeds and fruit, our cattle and furniture—and of course ourselves. But we human beings are also profiteers and robbers. Consider what we have done in the world. We—one species—have spread over the entire globe, inventing means of keeping alive by destroying life everywhere. Look how long it takes a tree to grow, we chop down whole forests to build or keep ourselves warm or make paper. Look at the endless number of plants we devour, as well as animals.

It is Man who is mainly responsible for disturbing the natural balance of species, which forms such a delicate network that, destruction of any races may create a disturbance with far-reaching results beyond our estimate. It is always interesting to contemplate a subject from a new angle and it would probably shatter a lot of our pet theories if we could have the insect's viewpoint.

An insect perhaps lives on a wild plant related to the cabbage. Man comes along and cultivates whole fields of cabbages. Picture the huge joy of that insect when instead of hunting among crowds of other plants for its particular food it finds masses spread out temptingly in a manner beyond its wildest dreams. Picture the joy with which that insect hurries off to take a wife and bring into the world as many generations as possible in the limited time at its disposal, so that they may all live a life of ease and luxury free from gnawing anxieties. Wouldn't insects be fools if they missed such a glorious opportunity! And insects are not fools.

A corn weevil—whose life has been spent in hunting for a grain here and a seed there—happens to find a granary, with immense piles of nice, dry corn: abundance without toil. Isn't it enough to make a corn weevil delirious with happiness? He loses no time, he goes ahead in a most systematic fashion. Then if the owner of that granary doesn't take drastic measures the robbers will not leave him the surplus desired.

Then nature takes a hand, for the corn weevils must not be permitted to multiply beyond a certain ratio in the balance of species. Man has introduced new conditions, nature proceeds to adjust them by increasing predators and parasites, which are the normal controls of the corn weevils and others that have multiplied too suddenly. All sorts of insects which people despise prove to be our very good friends in these new conditions by partially eliminating the pests which man has encouraged.

A race of insects becomes a pest one year, in the next the numbers may increase or still be high, but in the third year unless there is outside interference its own parasites will have reasserted their control. Parasites on the eggs, others on the larvæ and others again on the adults. The greater the numbers of the pests the stronger will be the armies of predators and parasites developed, which will control them. But the pest will not be entirely wiped out. No, merely readjusted to balance with other species. There are all the species to be balanced to take advantage of the favourable conditions which man has created. So the pest's numbers will be proportionate to the good food which man has spread out before them. It will still exist in numbers of which man probably will disapprove, taking a larger share of the crop than can be tolerated.

Agriculturists cannot be expected to take such a dispassionate view of the matter so they use chemical control, a drastic measure which brings a disadvantage in that it is liable to destroy predators and parasites as well as the pests. Chemicals are scattered from aeroplanes, chemicals are sprayed or atomized over the affected crops. Some measures are completely, others partially successful. Biological control is used as well which is the introduction of the predators and parasites from other localities into the affected area and this on the whole proves more successful.

When insects migrate in vast swarms man may be helpless to stop them or control the numbers in spite of all the modern methods of attack. He has to stand by and witness the destruction of his crops and own that the indomitable insect has got the upper hand. The accounts of these invasions bring it home to us more convincingly than by any other consideration how perfectly insects are equipped, scarcely vulnerable to our intelligent deliberate attacks, actually only vulnerable to their perfectly equipped parasites.

The structure of a locust is perfectly adapted to its rôle as a living engine of destruction. No dragon could be designed to play the part of a devouring beast so admirably. These insects are merely winged stomachs, with jaws. They are blessed with excellent digestion and their reproductive capacity is beyond praise. What more does a living engine of destruction need? Wings are capable of bearing them for thousands of miles during their astounding flights. As in all flying insects they have air sacs connected with the outer air to keep up the supply of oxygen. A very remarkable fact as already mentioned is that there is no special equipment for remaining in the air during such long periods of time, there is none indeed to distinguish them from those humdrum locusts that never leave the locality where they are born.

In these days locust swarms are no novelty, there is knowledge of the subject. We see them in photographs, on films, maps and graphs. We must go back to earlier days to find a good description of an invasion, of the wholesale destruction committed in a short time merely by force of numbers. A most vivid account, which I consider the best ever given, was published in 1875 by an eyewitness of a locust migration in Colorado.

"The insects came with the wind and alighted in the rain. The ground was covered two or three inches deep and glittered with their wings like a new dollar. Next day when they rose their wings would become entangled and they fell in matted heaps. Everywhere they alighted they tested with their jaws, and the noise of this continual crunching was more like the crackling of a prairie fire than anything with which I can compare it."

The size of swarms varies considerably and so does the density. Sometimes they fly in almost serried masses as close as possible without collision. But Charles Darwin in describing one which he had seen mentions his surprise when he waved a stick to find that the locusts were able to swerve aside and avoid it.

In South Africa several experiments have been made to utilize a swarm as food. It has been proved on analysis that locusts do contain a certain amount of fat.

In one very early account of an invasion in the first stage of locusts—the hoppers—before wings are developed, they were shovelled up and boiled in large vats with some idea of making use of them for poultry or cattle. When cold there was quite an inch of fat on the surface of the water, but no practical use could be found for it. Cattle, poultry and ostriches will feed upon locusts but soon tire of the diet, even insectivorous birds and mammals are soon glutted, long before a swarm has passed. In any case an insufficient number could be devoured to make an appreciable difference. The only foes that can decimate their numbers are those indefatigable little creatures—their parasites.

The vast numbers of locusts that perish during a migration cannot be estimated. One account of a swarm passing over the Red Sea is worth quoting. It was in the log of a sea captain who sailed through it. He wrote laconically a mere statement of facts but the narrative loses nothing on this account. Rather, it gains in histrionic effect. He wrote:

"For over five days the ship was passing through flying locusts. Her decks were overlaid with corpses of the insects many inches thick merely because they had collided with the rigging. It occupied two men's time all that while to sweep them off into the sea. The waves as far as eye could see were white with outspread wings of dead locusts as if the sea were covered in snow.

## Pests

"Such multitudes of them were drowned that where waves washed them ashore banks of them were formed over three feet high for miles along the coast. The stench of the dead was unbearable and was perceived in villages far inland."

And man is helpless against such hordes. He can only watch his territories being invaded and his crops vanishing. Fields devoured by locusts is such an accepted event that in these days nobody writes home about it. No descriptions can quite make those who have not had the experience understand the wretched conditions which have to be endured as well as the wholesale destruction. I quote once more, this time a description of locust swarms in the Ukraine in 1646 which is very graphic:

"It is not easy to express their numbers for all the air just now is full and darkened. I cannot better represent their flight to you than by comparing it with the flakes of snow in cloudy weather driven about by the wind. And when they alight upon the ground to feed the plains are all covered, and they make a murmuring sound as they feed, where in less than two hours they devour all close to the ground. Then, rising, they suffer themselves to be carried away by the wind. And when they fly, though the sun shines never so bright it is no lighter than when most cloudy.

"In June 1646, having stayed two months in a new town called Novogorod where I was building a citadel,

I was astonished to see so vast a multitude because they were hatched there that spring, and, being as yet scarce able to fly, the ground was all covered. And the air was so full of the flying forms that I could not eat in my chamber without a candle. All the houses were full of them even to the stables—barns, chambers, garrets, and cellars. I caused cannon powder and sulphur to be burnt to expel them but all to no purpose. When the door was opened they went out and still could flutter around and an infinite number came in.

"It was a troublesome thing when a man went abroad to be hit on the face by these creatures, sometimes on the nose, eyes or cheek, there was no opening one's mouth but some of them would get in. Yet all this was nothing to compare with the times when we wanted to eat for these creatures gave us no respite. When we went to cut a bit of meat we cut a locust with it. When a man opened his mouth to chew a morsel he was sure to chew one of them.

"I have seen them at night when they sit to rest that the roads were four inches thick of them one upon another. The horses would not trample over them unless they were driven on with much lashing, pricking up their ears and snorting and treading very fearful. The wheels of our carts and the feet of our horses bruising these creatures there came from them such a stink as not only offended the nose but the brain. I was not able to endure that stench but was forced to wash my nose in vinegar, and hold my handkerchief dipped in it continually to my nostrils."

Robert Southey's idea of swarming locusts clothes them picturesquely on the other hand and gives them quite another aspect:

> Onward they come, a dark continuous cloud
> Of congregated myriads numberless,
> The rushing of whose wings was as the sound
> Of a broad river headlong in its course
> Plunged from a mountain summit, or the roar
> Of a wild ocean in the autumn storm.

After all locusts are vegetarians, they may starve our livestock but they do not attack living animals, whereas all things living must flee for their lives before an invasion of army ants or driver ants as they are sometimes called. Small invasions can be dealt with but sometimes there is an attack by prodigious numbers. Nothing is safe from them which happens to be on their route and cannot take to flight, babies have been devoured piecemeal in their cradles.

A very detailed and interesting account of one of these invasions was given by a well-known naturalist, Arthur Loveridge, while collecting reptiles in German East Africa. One can realize the terror inspired by these formidable aggressive insects. The account was culled from his diary.

"June 3rd. At 8 A.M. I discovered that we were being

invaded by army ants, which were entering the stone-work of the house at half a dozen different points. Beetles were flying in numbers before the advancing hosts, frequently with one or more of the red furies attached to their hind legs. Wretched crickets and small grasshoppers were being dragged off, feebly waving the one or two legs that remained to them. The marmalade ants were driven from their hiding places and sought refuge among books and papers on my table. Jumping spiders cleared for their life with prodigious leaps, one black beetle was clinging to the table cloth, apparently they had passed him by.

"Soldier sentinels of these ants were stationed at intervals of two inches along the lines of the marching column, waiting with widely opened jaws for any disturbers.

"At 9 P.M. I procured wash-basin, soap dishes, etc., and placed them under the four legs of the bed which so far had not been invaded and filled them with water. Then I raised the mosquito net and jumped in to accomplish disrobing in some degree of comfort.

"June 4th. Towards sunset small lines issued from a hole at the base of the outside wall and entered another hole, a second line was going in the reverse direction. Neither company bore any spoils, and their procedure seemed aimless and foolish, unless indeed we suppose it was a practice route march for two companies to pass through each other without confusion. I have noticed this with these ants many scores of times.

"June 5th. I retired to bed and despite the fact that the walls and floors were a crawling mass of live ants I slept in confident security until 2.30 A.M. when I was awakened by the splashing of one of my crocodiles in their pen outside the house. Most of my creatures I had moved outside the previous day but thought that the young crocodiles in their tank could defy the army ants. The tortoises had also been left in their pen outside the house. Heroically I decided to rise and go to the rescue despite the ants on the floor.

"Untucking the net therefore I stretched out a hand to turn up the lamp and found an ant on the handle. Then I saw a few ants on my pillow and discovered two single lines moving up the net, one inside and the other outside the net. I examined the pans of water under the legs of the bed, across one of them at the head of the bed a company of sappers had thrown a bridge composed of living ants upon which their comrades were coming and so up the net! I hurriedly splashed out enough oil on the bridge to cause its collapse, and in the water many a gallant Horatius ant soldier lost its life.

"Then I went out to the crocodile cage. One poor beast about fifteen inches in length was revolving round and round in the water, belly and back being alternately uppermost, while all the time he threshed water with his tail in an effort to rid himself of his inexorable assailants. The edges of the rectangular pan—2 ft. by 1 ft.—were lined with a throng of onlooker ants which hurled themselves upon the crocodile whenever his struggles brought him near the side. I pulled him out by the tail and threw him twenty feet away. Running to the spot—which was free of ants—I picked him up with a pair of forceps and dropped him into a pan of drinking water. In the morning he had got rid of all the ants except one on each eyelid. These I picked off with forceps and got bitten in thanks. He felt very seedy for a day or two but survived his ordeal.

"Returning to the house I looked for the other crocodile but it had sought refuge beneath the hay, and as there was no movement or commotion going on I correctly concluded it was dead. Next day all the hay in the crocodile cage was burnt, it was a seething mass of ants. The skin and bones only of the crocodile were left, it was totally eaten up by the ants.

"The tortoises when I came out in the night, were making such a commotion inside their enclosure that I started in their direction, but the ground that lay between me and the tortoises was so alive with the ants that I very regretfully turned back.

"Once more I sought the shelter of my mosquito net on the outside of which there were still approximately two hundred ants which had been cut off from retreat by the collapse of the bridge. These I dislodged by striking the net sharply on the inside so that most of them fell on the floor. Some clung on however and to my disgust the workers made their way through the mesh of the net. I killed one in the very act of struggling through a mesh and half a dozen that had already done so. The big-jawed soldiers stayed outside. I killed the others one by one as they got in till I was left in comparative peace.

"My own immediate troubles being ended I listened to the sounds on the roof which were easy of interpretation. A rat, attacked, ran for its life with a frightened squeak, lost its foothold on the galvanised iron and rolled down, landing with a thump on the ground. Not so fortunate were the nestling rats—at least so I judged by a series of small squeaks which gradually grew fainter. It made me shudder to think of what an awful death these small creatures were dying. The bats had left on the first day. I found one dead clinging to the mosquito gauze of the window. Perhaps it died of fright for had the ants attacked it they would not have left one bone uncleaned.

"June 6th. With handfuls of blazing grass we swept up the lines of ants proceeding to the tortoise enclosure, and then went in to effect their release. To my relief the Box Tortoises were all alive. Their armour-plated forelegs were drawn in to protect the head in a most wonderful fashion. But they had had such a fright that none of them protruded its head while I was there.

The soft-shelled land tortoises on the other hand had fared badly. Many had a score of ants attached to them, one had its eyelids badly eaten. I dropped all these into a drum of water and then set a native to pick off the ants with forceps."

The only creatures which could really stand up to the formidable army ants, when crocodiles, mammals and human beings could only save themselves by getting outside the marching columns—were other ants! It is most interesting to learn that Loveridge on that occasion when invaded by these huge hordes saw them defied by stink ants.

"Later in the day I saw a pleasing sequel in a fight between army ants and stink ants. These lived in the house and had often put the former to flight. Beneath the doorstep where this affray took place a little heap of dirt and the heads of army ants caught my eye. I therefore watched the entrance to the hole outside. Presently a stink ant came to the opening and dropped an army ant head, then another emerged with a bit of grit, and a third with a head—and so on. I removed this dump and found that it was only the soldiers which had been beheaded, the workers' bodies were intact. I counted a hundred corpses, and estimated the remainder at seven hundred, which represented one day and a night's work."

So it was only the little fire ants and the stink ants which were able to defend themselves successfully from the notorious army ants, and make themselves respected by aggressive little villains buoyed up by mob courage. While man—not being blessed with armour-plated limbs like the box tortoise—had to use fire brands or else run away.

But now consider swarms of caterpillars which neither sting nor bite. We read of enormous areas laid waste by the army worms or cut worms, and how useless all efforts were to hinder the devastating march through the United States before methods of control had been studied and introduced. Here again personal experience only can give any idea of the intense discomfort of such an invasion on the top of all the losses.

This species is another example of a race demoralized by man's huge food-production schemes. It may have been a grass-feeder at one time. When in the United States large areas were put under cultivation it showed up as a major pest of liberal tastes. Cornfields multiplied and the army worm fed on corn. Cotton was cultivated and the army worm took to cotton. The far richer food and its plenitude caused racial variations which could take full advantage. There appeared one more generation per year—the range of diet was increased.

There is in fact very little indeed which can cause the army worm indigestion. The dietary includes—all kinds of grass, any kind of corn, not only leaf blades but the ear as well. Roots such as turnip, carrot, etc., do not come amiss, tomatoes, first the shoots and buds then the fruit, then any part which remains.

It attacks such juicy fruit in a very curious manner, for it actually lives inside, burrowing a way through, eating out a tunnel in a voracious manner without pause. As it feeds, part of the pulp passes right through the caterpillar and is deposited behind it closing the entrance to its moist burrow, so in a short time it is living in a cavity large enough to contain it comfortably and continuing to feed on the walls of its chamber. Secure from interruption it continues to feed on the entire contents of the tomato leaving only the outer skin. And the only sign that there is a living creature inside is the greenish matter sealing the entrance. If you do not notice this you are liable to have a shock.

When in certain years these caterpillars by some means evaded their natural controls they were beyond being checked by any measures man could devise. In some years there were exceptionally bad seasons; this was while economic entomology was still in its initial experimental stage.

Its appearance brought despair and enormous losses to farmers, horticulturists and market gardeners as may be well imagined. For creatures of such large appetite and catholic tastes to show themselves in huge numbers spelt calamity on a large scale, and by force of numbers they would carry the day.

The accounts of these advances scarcely sound like

sober fact. As they devoured crops, famine drove them on. One great avalanche of caterpillars in the United States was 85 miles broad and 30 miles long. Only a very wide stream or river baulked them. If canals were cut the vanguard fell in but the army still marched on. When the canal was filled up with corpses it crossed on the top of them; so it was of little use making trenches, the pressure of the multitudes behind was too great. If the first line paused those following merely crawled over them, the hordes were in depth in some places as well as width and length.

At first birds started to feed on them, fowls were driven out among them and accounted for some but they were all soon sated. Pigs at first appeared to enjoy them, hopefully herds were put out in the fields but they were speedily glutted and would not touch them afterwards though they killed thousands by trampling them into the soil. But of what use to slaughter thousands when there were miles of them behind always pressing on, driven by hunger?

Where the caterpillars stopped to feed on low plants it was said that not even a stick could be put down between individuals, it was one great carpet of caterpillars. The one remedy which did succeed where small crops were in jeopardy was to make very wide trenches filled with burning straw. There would be a moving mass of caterpillars eight or ten deep all round these but the masses were diverted in time.

A description of one area after such a visitation is worth quoting. It was written by a farmer. The invasion had lasted nearly two months; caterpillars at different stages of growth succeeding one another. Whole pastures were so covered with them that one could not put down a finger on any spot without touching a caterpillar. One heap of those that were slaughtered was measured. It contained ten bushels of squashed caterpillars. That alone suggests why ordinary means of combating them were abandoned. Only total extermination with complete destruction of corpses would have had any lasting results.

"They moved at a great rate when on the march to new feeding grounds and were only still when feeding. They filled houses and the occupants fled. They would go straight up the wall of a house in such a compact column that nothing showed of the building. Some would climb a stalk of corn and eat below the ear until it fell and it did not remain long on the ground.

"There were fields of corn on the ploughland of Haverhill and Newbury, standing so thick, large and tall that in some instances it was difficult to see a man standing more than one rod in the field from the outermost row, but in ten days from the first appearance of the caterpillars nothing remained of this corn but the bare stalks."

The question whether it is possible to exterminate any pest has been answered by the signal victory over the malaria mosquito in Cyprus in modern times. Being an island it was an ideal area for such an experiment with such a wide neutral belt around it. But at the same time it had to be treated yard by yard, vegetation tooth-combed, every drop of surface water examined before every mosquito and every larva and egg was destroyed. Breeding places on a mountainous rocky island of that description may be anywhere, and if even one part of the mosquitoes had survived the trouble would have re-started.

So the work of extermination was extremely arduous, but it succeeded. It is one of the few examples of man's complete mastery of an insect race which had become a pest. The work was very well organized and carried out with enthusiasm. Expenses were borne by the population cheerfully for they realized what the achievement would mean and weighed it against the cost.

The entire island was parcelled out into areas which were the responsibility of those selected for the job. Fifteen square miles was the largest sized area and the smallest were eight. These are all extensive plots for such a survey where every crack and indentation of the soil which could hold rain-water must be treated. Cyprus species of Anopheline mosquitoes fortunately do not breed in tree holes which collect rain-water so it was not necessary to examine the trees as well, but mature mosquitoes rest in any vegetation. Otherwise the survey was confined to the ground. But what difficult ground!

Two mountain ranges and plains between. Water

in rocks might have an entrance only large enough to admit a mosquito, so these must be sprayed. Some had to be sprayed from a height of at least sixty feet because there was no access. Pockets in high faces of rock were a problem, sprayers had to be lowered on ropes.

Hunting the adults was a different sort of game. Anyone who has tried to clear a house of mosquitoes knows that they seem imbued with a diabolical cunning. They secrete themselves in most unlikely places, in dark corners and cracks, and refuse to be dislodged until the right hour for them to sally forth voluntarily when the house is supposed to be rid of the last one.

High buildings had to be tackled, castles, temples, churches. There were many difficult niches to reach in these. D.D.T. was an immense help, but only because every member of the extermination brigade realized that all their work would be thrown away if one crack happened to be overlooked. Not one was overlooked, not one individual escaped. It was a costly experiment, but the cost was quite immaterial when it was a question of ridding a population of such a scourge as malaria. The results are even greater than the victory over the yellow fever mosquito in the Panama Zone because mosquitoes can re-enter it from outside areas. It is greater than the victory over the malaria mosquito in New Guinea during the Japanese invasion because that too was local, only camps were immune through spraying with D.D.T.

## Pests

This is a complete triumph, and our just pride in it emphasizes how rarely we have occasion to boast that a pest has been annihilated by man.

As for the extent of damage to our crops and domestic animals, it has been roughly estimated that almost fifty per cent of the entire world's food products for the human race is appropriated by the indomitable insect. When we take into account the wholesale destruction of crops by locusts and the incalculable casualties among wild game as well as domestic herds by the tsetse fly we can perceive that this estimate is not exaggerated. With regard to agriculture it has recently been stated that ten per cent of crops, even in pest-controlled areas, is lost, and outside these areas twenty per cent.

# 8. Social Organizations

W̱E ARE TOLD THAT THE HUMAN RACE made great strides forward in progressive development directly man began to grow food and store it. Communities formed and family life became village life, and so, with labour shared and assigned to special castes of workers, there were endless advantages not enjoyed by nomadic races. Defence was one of these advantages and the art of fighting battles also was practised.

It is interesting to trace an analogy with insects. When some insect groups evolved social habits their activities increased a hundredfold. Food storage, and —among ants—the development of agriculture, horticulture and dairy farming show what a great deal can be accomplished without intelligence. The bees, wasps, ants and termites (which are popularly called white ants) are the four social groups. Of these the ants have far outstripped the others in their enormous diversity of occupations. Ants are all social, no solitary species—without queens—have ever been found. There are the parasitic species which are without workers but they must be considered separately, they belong to the social groups.

New instincts were bound to be evolved by social organizations. Defence of the home, defence of the queen and broods, building and repairs, tending the young through early stages, collecting food and feeding all inmates of the nest including guests, all these employments do not come into the daily régime of solitary insects so we are certain that appropriate instincts had to develop at the same time.

Plenty of insects perform very elaborate tasks in preparation for the next generation but when the eggs are laid responsibility ceases. The female alone has carried out all this preliminary work. In the next higher grade the male helps his mate. Some beetles related to the sacred scarabs do this. Together they dig an immense shaft, about five feet deep, in soil. Then the male collects animals' droppings at the top of the shaft, works them into pellets of the right size and sends them down to the female who waits at the bottom. She shreds the stuff, packs it and lays eggs on it. The brood when they hatch feed on this and the mother stays with them until they come out of pupæ and escorts them to the mouth of the burrow before leaving them.

Mothers of several kinds of insects remain with the young, some crickets and earwigs do this, but there is not any communal life even where females live near together, making their nests side by side but only passing their neighbours on busy thoroughfares. There is not even a combining of forces to resist a common enemy.

It is the paramount female—the queen—with neuter workers which constitute the basic machinery of a community of social insects; she is the axis on which that little world revolves.

As far as is known the only case where the royal spouse assists the queen in starting a colony is among termites. He helps her to excavate the first cavity where eggs are laid. It is a modest little room to contain the first batch, and when these hatch the larvæ are tended by both parents until they have passed through the first stages of growth. Both give up this duty and the queen devotes the rest of her life to the business of laying eggs. She becomes a specialized egg-laying machine and by and by is built into a compartment which is just large enough to hold her enormously distended body. Passages lead into it but only workers can use the entrances which are small.

The entombed queen never leaves it again, as fast as eggs are laid they are carried away and tended elsewhere.

Queens have been known to live for ten years though probably this is not a record, and it is estimated that they lay 120,000,000 eggs in a lifetime.

It is a very busy life that termites lead. They are terribly destructive to our buildings of all kinds but perform universal service by carrying rotting fibre underground and thus enrich the soil. Their food is the cellulose of all timber which is collected directly growth has ceased. Termites never touch healthy living trees but they know when any wood is beginning to rot. If they cannot get across by working inside they will build neat long tunnels of clay outside on the bark to the place which is decaying, where they can work without exposing themselves to their many enemies.

It is marvellous to see the hard-bodied kinds which need not work in galleries flowing in a broad stream five or six inches wide in millions along their trails, up and down roots and rocks to a doomed limb where there is cellulose which may be collected.

The cement that they use for building some of their outside nests is of the finest type imaginable because it passes through the termites' digestive machinery first. Termite nests can be ground to powder to provide cement for building purposes. Usually the labour required is too costly, for the nests are extremely hard.

The most satisfactory use for it that I have seen is in making tennis courts. Collected locally, pounded and laid thickly over the ground there is little cost; rain does the rest and the court only needs rolling. It is more pleasant to play on than asphalt; there is a certain elasticity about it.

Where there are few termites or none such as high up on mountains their industry is missed. All the ground is encumbered with rotten wood; generations of it slowly disintegrating. For human beings it is difficult and sometimes dangerous, for in treading on one log you may fall through several which would have been cleared long before had there been termite nests in that neighbourhood.

So forests benefit, but not human habitations for all dry wood is claimed as a right. Boards, beams, rafters, furniture, fences—all fall into the same category and must be watched for the first sign of attack. And signs are difficult to find. Perhaps the first warning is when the owner of a house puts his hand on a rail and it collapses under him. He leans against a cupboard and it falls in, or the roof gives way and he finds beams are nothing but a thin shell. There are chemicals for treating all timber. Concrete foundations to a house are essential wherever there are termites.

Scent is the directive for finding dry wood but there may be other senses used as well. It is wonderful how quickly termite workers locate it. I remember once leaving a little wooden box all night on an iron table on a veranda. In the morning at daybreak I went to fetch it and as I was picking it up there was a movement on the table. It made me look more closely, and I discovered that it was the head of a termite at the entrance of a gallery extending from the ground through the veranda and up the iron table. This had nearly reached its objective and certainly had not been there the evening before; it had all been built during the night. That the termites discovered that there was a whitewood box on the table when they never expose themselves points to a very acute sense of smell.

Not only is there a constant quest for wood but for water too and this will lead them to tunnel to great depths. Some years ago termites were found doing serious damage to lead-sheathed cables in conduits of the Panama Canal locks. The telephone service was found to be very unsatisfactory, and when investigations were made fifty feet of damaged cable had to be replaced and precautions taken to keep it free of termites. A secretion of the soldier termites had pierced the cable. This was a considerable feat for such small insects. They passed through cables to reach water beyond.

Queens of the other groups are active. None of them are incarcerated like termites. What is so interesting is that all the many hereditary instincts needed by workers are inherent in the queen who does not take part in the labours for which these instincts are needed. Workers are not all neuter, some can lay eggs, but the commencement of a new community devolves on the queen. It used to be thought that there must be some difference in the eggs which led to their producing different grades—queens, males, ordinary workers or soldiers. But it was discovered that the determination of the castes depended upon the food which was given to the young larvæ, so the development of these is the responsibility of the workers. It has been worked out what percentage of protein, fat and sugar is needed for each grade. Queens of course require the richest diet for the sake of the supply of eggs being maintained. On the worker ants is the responsibility for keeping the population of a nest within limits proportionate to the food available. This is more simple than it sounds. Supposing there is a food shortage (and worker ants are in the best position to be aware of this) they will feed their population with some of the eggs. This is not to appease their personal appetite but to provide extra nourishment for the community. It may be regarded as ploughing back the profits into the business.

Worker ants lead a life of self abnegation which probably cannot be excelled. All day long from daybreak to dark they are hurrying from one task to another. There is no pause for rest or refreshment but they get a sip here and there which keeps them going as they work, and perhaps change of occupation may take the place of recreation. All personal needs are suppressed. They even keep a separate stomach—a crop—at the service of the rest of the colony. This has been aptly named the social stomach to distinguish it from what we may call the personal stomach. Not until food has actually passed into the digestive system can ant workers call it their own. There are few human social workers who would go to those lengths.

Semi-digested food is returned to the crop to be fed drop by drop to larvæ or anybody of the colony who needs nourishment. The distribution has been watched by feeding coloured syrup to workers. An ant's abdomen will expand when it drinks a quantity and the colour will show through. In the nest workers will come to beg from the replete ants, vibrating their antennæ and putting out their tongues. Not that much of the food will be for themselves but will be passed on. The different coloured gasters are easy to follow and give a very good idea of the division of labour among workers. It fills one with admiration too to see those thousands passing and repassing in a nest each to its special allotted task. And never a collision. Occasionally one can notice hesitation or a halt but another worker will at once stop to investigate the cause. There will be a drumming of antennæ, then the doubtful worker has received some sort of information and joins the rushing throng. Workers in other groups besides ants have specified tasks and all have defensive instincts.

Even the tiny stingless bees have these social defensive instincts. I have seen a nest when ants were trying to enter it but were driven away. There was a spout-shaped entrance to the nest which was in a tree. It had been fabricated by the workers and had taken over two weeks to build of moss, bark, lichen, debris of all sorts and a kind of gum. When completed it looked just like a broken piece of rotten bough. It was only when the little bees were flying into it that it could be noticed that it was not growing out of the tree naturally.

Ants are deadly enemies of these bees. I noticed that two worker ants had run down the top of the spout and one was almost inside. No bees were to be seen and I thought this must be the beginning of a raid by ants, but the first ant hesitated, the second seemed to get a whiff of something it did not like and drew back its head. The first came out again from the mouth of the entrance and both ran away as fast as they could.

I took my electric torch and looked down the spout. A couple of inches from the entrance were four little bees with their mandibles wide open, behind them were two more rows and others were coming up from the nest. I judged that it was the smell of formic acid which had deterred the ants. I could just perceive it, to them it may have been overpowering, for there are formic acid glands connected with the mandibles of stingless bees.

There is no need to point out that hive bees and any wasps will resent interference with the nest, for most people can remember occasions when this was very evident. But an observation hive of bees provides unfailing interest, wasps' nests too are entertaining, and worth risking a few stings to watch. It is best, if the opportunity is favourable, to watch the same community day by day. You recognize what a number of different duties are undertaken by queen and workers, males are never much in evidence. It is interesting to watch different stages of the community's development; if any workers can be marked one learns a great deal.

I got quite fond of one wasp community that I met with in New Guinea when I stayed for some time in a small government rest-house in the Owen Stanley Mountains. It had roof and walls thatched with coconut leaves. There was only one room with a broad veranda all round it and, at the end of a covered passage, kitchen and bathroom.

There were eight different kinds of wasps living in the house, three of them built fairly large nests. One was in the bathroom wall but they were quite amiable. One with striped black and yellow faces built under the veranda—they were inoffensive. But one kind with yellow faces were rather touchy—that was the community I was most interested in, they had started a nest in a corner of the veranda where I arranged my table.

It was only a small nest of about nine cells when I arrived. The workers were busy all day long adding to it, at work on tree trunks or on the veranda chopping off bits of dry bark. They pulped it with their jaws into a sort of papier mâché, this they rolled into a ball and flew back to the nest with it balanced between their chin and forelegs. When the grubs began to hatch out in the nest the workers hunted for insects of all kinds, particularly caterpillars, to feed them on. That was pulped too and brought to the nest in a ball.

There was a constant going and coming with a great deal of fuss. And like most fussy people they thought their own affairs much more important than anybody else's.

The business of feeding wasp grubs looks very irregular. If they were not fastened by the tail into the cells they would fall out for they hang upside down. But they are firmly fixed. Nurse workers feed them individually making the round of the cells and putting their heads inside each to give the grub a mash of chopped up caterpillar. When the grubs are old enough nearly to fill the cell they put out their heads from the entrance when they are hungry. If workers are making their round and a grub does not appear then it is passed over and has to go without. That is what looks so irregular and I think that is why when they are mature some wasps are so much smaller than others. It is most noticeable among the workers. There are females which are much bigger, those are the queens, for in this genus (*Polistes*) there are several queens instead of one to each community.

When there were several queens and enough workers in that nest they began to branch off and set up establishments for themselves. They did not leave the house,

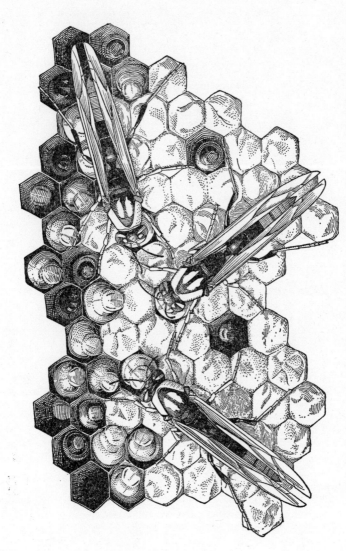

The wasp grubs put out their heads when they are hungry

and they were a real nuisance because they started nests
in all the most sheltered spots.

Coconut thatching is supposed to keep out rain for
ten years, but that house was more than ten years old
and heavy rain would stream through in places. I had
a tarpaulin sheet over my hammock, and chairs and
tables for my work were under the most solid parts of
the roof.

That is where I clashed with the wasps. We all wanted
the same conditions. I had up-ended a case in one corner
of the veranda as a table with another case to sit on.
One morning I got stung and there were several workers buzzing round my face. I could not think what had
made them so bad-tempered all of a sudden. Then I
discovered that a very small bunch of cells had been
built inside the box that I was sitting on and they were
defending it. I scraped it off but the workers defended
the foundations. So in the end I turned up the case
and left it outside in the rain to cool their tempers until
they lost interest in it.

It is rather dark for work in that type of house and
the best position was on the veranda. So I put my
largest table in the driest place there, which happened
to be near the wasps' nest. As I sat there writing notes
or preserving insects there was a continual traffic of busy
wasps.

It is curious that wasps which have such marvellous
instincts for their delicate tasks do not seem to know

when they have too heavy a load to carry. They can judge bulk but not weight. A worker would alight on the top veranda rail with a ball of food, and on the nest a group of nurse-workers would be waiting for it. They have to divide it and then feed the grubs. I would see a bunch of little yellow faces following every movement of the one bringing food. Then with the heavy load it would try to reach them, miss the nest and with a wobbly flight make for the farther part of the veranda. And all the disappointed yellow faces took up a position on the other side of the nest, and waited again till the load was adjusted and the worker had another try with perhaps the same result. I have even seen them fly outside again without depositing their load. This happened frequently, they wanted to carry as much as could be balanced no matter how it weighed them down.

Then one worker began to make use of me, others followed her example. They found that I made a convenient half-way landing post a little higher than the rail from which they could take off with a better chance of reaching the nest. This became too much of a nuisance. I would see a movement on my shoulder and discover a wasp adjusting its load. Or they would settle on my head and get a hair entangled in a ball of mashed grubs and then be unreasonably aggrieved when they found it attached. I felt they were taking my co-operation too much for granted so though it was not so convenient for me I pulled my table back against the wall. There I was out of the line of traffic.

The effect was pathetic. They would come and hover in front of me carrying a load, as if they were saying, "Why don't you put out your arm? Don't you see how you're hindering me. And all the children waiting to be fed!"

I hardened my heart at first but finally put out a chair instead, and they soon got into the habit of using that as a traffic halt.

The community was still quite small when there was an attack by a dangerous neighbour, a large brown hornet almost twice their size. I reckoned there were eight workers then, five used to stop on the nest while three hunted for food. I saw a hornet come in and hover in front of the nest examining it while the five workers cowered at the back of the combs. Then it flew off again. It did that several days running and when its deep booming hum was heard the yellow faces huddled together miserably.

Just as seven wasp grubs were fully grown and the nurse-workers had sealed them up in their cells ready to pupate the hornet came again. It seemed to know all about them and set to work in a most business-like manner, it found a cell, tore it open with its big jaws, dragged out the fat grub and flew off with it. In twenty minutes it was back for another victim, at the end of the day all seven had gone, only empty torn cells remained. The workers walked all over them mournfully examining the damage. In a few days they repaired them. But they hadn't made an attempt to defend their infants after all that trouble in rearing them. They had just sat and looked on while the murderer carried out that foul deed. I was disgusted with them.

Then a few weeks later it happened again. I imagine it was the same hornet because it flew straight to that corner but this time it had a different reception. In the meanwhile another batch of workers had emerged. The hum of the enemy brought them all crowding to the nest; three flew to meet it. There were about eighteen altogether. The big bully came swaggering along and was attacked, three settled on its back stinging hard, and when it flew away in a zigzag they were hanging on to its legs and stinging with all their might.

I never saw such a complete discomfiture. This counter-attack must have been completely unexpected. I rejoiced with the yellow faces. No doubt they were aware of their increased numbers and this may have given them a sort of mob courage. But they routed the enemy so completely and in such a short time that it was surprising they had put up no defence at all on the previous occasion.

It occurred to me that the change in their behaviour may be accounted for by the fact that for the first raids there were only nurse-workers at home on the nest, the others were foraging as usual. But the enemy was routed after many more of the foraging workers had emerged and were at home, they would naturally be more valiant.

That ants too have instincts for defending the home needs no emphasis. In tropical forest on every hand are aggressive little patriots ready to challenge any intruder no matter the size that dares to come near the nest. Some sting, many bite or squirt formic acid and there are terrifying attitudes adopted by some species which are part of the defensive measures. The most curious form that I saw of this type of protection was the attitudes of workers belonging to a certain group of ants if the leaves with the nests inside were touched.

They built in a climbing palm which spreads over the trees. Leaves die at the tip turning brown and dry, at the same time they partly curl, inside these the ants make nests and set up rather small communities. A touch on any part of the trees brings stout defenders outside to patrol the nest, spraying formic acid and waving or revolving the pair of forelegs at the same time. It is a most curious sight, but it is wise not to linger in the neighbourhood when once the nests are disturbed, because the ants are not satisfied with trying to frighten off a stranger but will let themselves fall to the ground then race across in the direction of the enemy. Their bite is very painful.

Among masses of evidence of ants' communal works it is difficult to select the most remarkable. The fact that is most striking is what highly specialized delicate tasks are assigned to workers. An impressive example is the method of fungus culture to produce an edible crop. Among the ants which go in for this kind of horticulture a special caste of gardeners has evolved who are entrusted solely with the care of fungus beds.

Fungus-growing ants seem to have made a great success of this form of horticulture for some of the nests are enormous. They are only found in the tropics and, though everybody had seen part of their work in collecting leaves from trees and had suffered from this habit, the highly specialized part of the work was not understood for many years. The largest are called parasol ants from their habit of carrying green leaves larger than themselves, held aloft as if to keep off the sun.

Huge excavations are made by colonies, resulting in very large heaps of soil above ground. From these, long trails of ants sally forth to collect leaves. It is usual to see two trails side by side of unladen workers going out and another trail of laden workers returning, like narrow fast-flowing black and green rivulets. It is the soft, large-leaved trees which are visited and many a planter sees with anguish some cherished shrub in his garden stripped bare.

For a long time it was taken for granted that the leaves were the food of ants underground, but there is a far more wonderful explanation. It is a skilful scientific method of horticulture which is carried out instinctively in these nests and in those of other ants that have the same habits.

Large chambers are prepared down below, the leaves are cut up into small pieces and beds of them are piled on the floor, mixed with other debris until it becomes a fine spongy mass. The next event is that spores of fungus are carefully sown over these beds when they are ready, and from them appears the first stage of fungus growth which is like a network of white threads. The fungus gardeners are tiny ants which form a caste exclusively devoted to this work, they are never seen above ground. Exactly what they do to the fungus is not known but instead of the next stage appearing in forms which we call toadstools the beds become covered with clusters of curious little swellings which are named *bromatia*. When these appear, young larvæ are brought from the nurseries to browse on this exclusive food like flocks of lambs, the nurse-ants carrying them back again when they are judged to have had enough. No fungus in the wild state produces *bromatia*. Mycologists have tried to do so but have not succeeded because they cannot treat the fungus with the special ingredient which the little gardeners apparently produce from their own bodies. It is not one species of fungus that is so treated, for the spawn of many different kinds have been identified from the ants' fungus beds.

A touch of romance is added by the fact that queen ants when they leave the nest for the marriage flight carry with them as their dowry a few fungus spores in their cheek pouches, sufficient to start the first fungus beds of their new homes.

Honey ants have taken a special line of development. Some of the workers have evolved social stomachs which can be distended to an enormous size so that they can act as living honey barrels to store food for the colony. They are too heavy to walk about so are suspended by their claws in rows in a nest where other workers can go to them when food is required.

All these very different habits require distinct series of instincts to deal with the work. It is futile to conjecture how they started, what for instance can have impelled the first ant to make use of the silk of their larvæ to weave the edges of leaves together so that the nest was secure? How did ants begin to make bridges? It is known that certain species can span a gap by clinging to each other in a living chain. This is done very methodically and a trail of workers will pass over it as long as it is needed. Then just as methodically the bridge disintegrates again.

When we consider examples of what ants can accomplish they appear so intelligent it is mystifying to see some action which looks to us extraordinarily stupid. Who has not watched an ant labouring towards the nest with some unwieldy load and taking a great deal of unnecessary trouble to engineer it over objects off the route. They will haul it up a grass bent only to find when they reach the top that this is not the way home but is a blind alley. Then they will either bring it all the way down again or drop it and have to spend a great deal of time in hunting for it. Waste of time and waste of energy, thinks the human onlooker—who can call ants' ways wonderful when they behave so idiotically?

This aimless wandering in nine cases out of ten is the result of losing a scent path. Ant workers are guided almost entirely by their olfactory organs and not by their eyes which only see dimly. When off the beaten track to the nest they blunder about until they fall in with it again. There are other occasions too when instincts followed precisely lead them astray.

When catching some workers on clay soil, by accident I pressed one into the soft ground and so left it to see whether its comrades would come to the rescue. They soon discovered the head with indignantly waving antennæ and several workers collected round it. They pulled at a leg and could not get it free so gave that up. Then, after much drumming with their antennæ on the victim, five of them together pulled at its head until it came off, when they bore it off to the nest without being unduly concerned that only half of the ant had been rescued.

After a battle the enemies' heads are cut off and carried separately into the victors' nest though their use is not obvious, so those workers were merely reverting to a different series of instincts in solving the problem of disinterring their friend.

Side by side with stupid acts are the exceptionally sagacious solutions to domestic problems which are mainly due to leaders. There are definite leaders among workers, not distinguishable yet to the fore in any catastrophe or hitch in the organization. It is probable that these are older workers. For broods succeed one another periodically but some individuals may outlive many broods. There is certainly some directing of labour, workers can be noticed carrying some of a new brood to the spot where labour is needed. The longer an ant lives the more experiences it will accumulate and this explains the difference in behaviour among any group.

Once when I was marking some workers I put a dab of white paint on four of them. The paint being thick they were lifted on the brush but seemed undisturbed and continued their meal directly they were put on the meat again. Three behaved like this but the fourth's reaction was quite different. When restored to the ground it bit the brush, then rushed at one ant that was feeding and dragged it away from the meat. Then it was not satisfied that this was the cause of its having been hoisted in the air, so it stood by the nearest trail interrupting the stream of workers, challenging them and catching one by the leg. This worker happened to be loaded but it was obliged to put down its load. An exchange of information followed, each drumming on the other's head. Whether this had a calming effect cannot be shown but the excitement died down and the aggrieved ant returned to the meat. Here were four individuals each receiving the same treatment and one of them gave a quite different reaction.

There are many different kinds of insects which are received in an ant community as guests and tended as if one of the family. This curious institution of certain privileged inmates where the majority of outsiders are fiercely excluded is explained by their exuding something which is agreeable to ants, and they are therefore tolerated as a source of food. Not all come under this category but some may deceive their hosts by scent and have nothing to offer in return for the security of the nest. They live and breed in a nest and their eggs and larvæ are tended.

Among the beetles is one species which when ready to pupate ought to burrow in soil. But the ant workers treat these pupæ as they do their own, arranging them in heaps on the surface of the soil according to date and inspecting them daily. These pupæ never develop and have to be cast away on the communal rubbish heap, except for a few which escape the kindly meant ministrations and get into soil or debris unnoticed. This again is a curious perversion of social instincts which proves that they are by no means infallible.

# 9. Instincts and Tropisms

Simplest actions of any are the reflex actions. In the lowliest types of the animal kingdom—those that have no nervous system—no other action is needed in their very simple lives. Something touches them, they withdraw, they are attracted towards food and imbibe it, they procreate their kind. That roughly is the sum total of their existence, a very monotonous one.

Even the simplest types of insect have much more interesting lives than this for they all have nervous systems, but there are simple systems and others more advanced which lead to very different behaviour. By means of sense organs of manifold designs each order of insects receives impressions which may not concern insects of another order, and those impressions are thereby converted into agents to enable them to perform their tasks.

So then, an insect gets some message from the outside world—a butterfly receives through its olfactory organs the scent of nectar. There is automatic response through the nerves which is translated into action. Nerve cells are all paired, both of the pair are concerned but each has a different rôle. The sensory nerves receive the message direct from the olfactory organ, and transmit it to the motor nerves which pass it on to the particular muscles concerned—then muscular action follows.

Results can be seen at once. The message was to the tightly coiled proboscis to relax, other muscles and nerves are affected and the insect drinks. Next the digestive system takes over. More muscles and nerves come into play with digestive secretions which are not visible. The whole machinery was set in motion by the scent of the nectar producing a reflex action.

Actions would all be simple if they were merely in response to a stimulus, there would be repetitions of the same kind. But nerves possess memory so the impression of a sensation if often repeated will remain, which results in one set of nerves always being affected in the same way. Since nerves are paired they can re-stimulate one another, and evoke an action without the need of a fresh stimulating of the sense organ every time—one is sufficient.

It is by this means that the wonderful instinctive habits have been built up, a long series each prompting the next following in their right order and the whole chain starting from the one sensation. By nerve memory habits are carried on from one generation to the next. So we see what is really an astonishing proceeding, the newly-hatched caterpillars behaving exactly as the last generation of caterpillars did, and this is no more wonderful than the fact that young birds reared in a cage build nests in the same manner as their parents.

The behaviour of female insects is always interesting because much of it does not serve them personally but the next generation. The butterfly which has been feeding on nectar one day by automatic response, will pass the same kinds of flowers next day and they may waft their aroma at her in vain, she ignores them. But certain leaves which are not her food are now her quest, she searches for them ruled only by that one sensation—the scent of the leaves. She may have perceived it from some distance away. When she has located the plant her eggs are deposited on the leaves so that the brood may be fed.

What has caused this change? Whence this new directive? Not from the environment for that is the same as yesterday, but from within. The butterfly has mated. There has been a rearrangement of chromosomes, a rearrangement of electrons of the nerves, and her behaviour changes. She drops one agent and takes up another to provide for the progeny which she would never recognize as her own if she saw them.

## Instincts and Tropisms

Any kind of provision for the future among insects is astonishing because it looks so wise, so purposeful, although we know that it is instinctive behaviour based on reflex actions. Instincts of caterpillars or other larvæ are astonishing too because at that stage insects are not in possession of all the faculties which they inherit when mature.

There are certain caterpillars which spin their cocoons among leaves where they have been feeding. Generally they make use of the flat surface of leaf and construct the cocoon against it, sometimes more than one leaf is used. When the time comes to pupate, they start the operation by first reinforcing the pedical of the leaf, binding it with silk wound round the nearest twigs as well. This is such a wise precaution that one could believe that the caterpillars know what they are doing. When leaves dry and fall off in autumn the insect might be in dire peril while it is comatose undergoing transformation. So it makes this use of its abundant supply of silk and remains safely above prowling mice and other enemies. Actually the cocoons are more visible to human eyes among bare twigs when once we have learnt these habits, but human prowlers are not such a menace as their natural enemies. Caterpillars of the wild silk moths of North America have this habit and as they are large the whole proceeding can be seen clearly. It is a long business. The caterpillar examines all the leaves in its immediate neighbourhood touching each with its palps—

the tactile organs of the mouth—until the choice is made, and then marches to the nearest twig and begins there, working back to the leaf itself.

The marvellous camouflage of some races results from simple instinctive actions. Attitude is of primary importance but muscles are being used which are not needed in the normal actions of moving and feeding and the other events of their everyday life. Two beetles may be sitting on the same tree trunk, a stag beetle and a weevil. You tap sharply on the wood. Response is immediate because that tap may signify danger but the response made by each beetle is totally different. The stag beetle stiffens slightly and opens its mandibles, the weevil lays its antennæ flat against the head, doubles up all its legs and falls to the ground. There it will stay looking like a clod of earth or fragment of wood—anything in fact rather than a beetle—until time has been given to allow an enemy to materialize. If there is no other alarming movement, in a few moments it will come to life, unfold all its limbs and walk away. The stag beetle will relax its rigorous attitude, close its mandibles and proceed with its occupations.

Both of these are beetles, they belong to the same order, but the same outside stimulus has produced entirely different instinctive reactions, which are automatic responses by their muscles through a stimulus of the nerves.

Even among insects which feign death like the weevil,

there are different sets of muscles brought into use. Some of the timid inoffensive races of ants have this habit but they do not take the same attitude as a weevil being endowed with a more flexible body. Antennæ are laid flat, the abdomen is curved and the head and thorax fitted against it. It is very difficult to recognize an ant which has rolled itself into a ball.

In one tropical species the nest is underground with a red clay porch at the entrance. The workers are reddish brown and when they run about on clay it is only the movement which betrays them. Many a time when collecting them I have had great trouble in locating them directly they were still. If it has rolled itself up into a ball it is impossible to guess which is ant among fragments of clay on the ground. I have always ended by collecting clay where I saw a worker and when I had a handful examining it all under a lens. After some minutes there will be a movement, a worker will put out one antenna tentatively to see whether the coast is clear then the abdomen is straightened and the legs unfolded.

There is another race which takes the same rolled-up attitude, these ants make a nest inside the stems of tree ferns. My first introduction to them was when I was cutting up hollow stems to look for beetles and crickets on a mountain of the New Hebrides. I was not expecting to find ants, and there was no nest, a few workers were either sheltering from rain for it was a very wet day, or they may have been on a hunting raid.

As I split open the stem fifteen ants rolled out on to a white cloth with other insects and I did not recognize them. They had shining black heads like enamel and rough red bodies. They looked like a fragment of some beetle stuck on to a bit of pith or soil. It was not until I had one in my hand and was trying to lift the supposed fragment that I found I was trying to pull an ant's head from its body. This was too embarrassing, the ant raised an antenna to find out what was going on and betrayed the camouflage. It was perfect.

In those cases of mimicry where insects belonging to different orders resemble one another, it is necessary for the mimic to adopt not only the pattern and colour but attitudes and habits of the model including muscular reactions.

Insects must be looked upon as perfect little machines compelled to make a certain response to a certain impulse, guided, controlled, and driven like all the rest of the animal world by forces which we call their agents, along racial standardized lines of development. And among the tyrannical forces which direct all their actions we have most interesting examples of what are known as tropisms.

These too are agents. Insects have evolved something which puts them at certain times under the influence of tropisms. While in such a tropic condition all other instincts are temporarily suspended. The insect is in the grip of a force which will not relax until a certain action has been accomplished. For the time being they are completely dominated and yet at another time when not in that condition the very thing which acted upon their sense organs so tyrannically will have no effect. It has ceased to be an agent.

The word "tropism" was first used by botanists. Later it was discovered that some of the animal world show tropic reactions. Tropisms are the enforced movements made by plants responding to outside forces—light, heat, moisture, chemicals and gravitation. The roots of a plant strike downwards because they are geotropic, it is the force of gravitation which is attracting them towards the earth's centre—the shoots grow upwards in a contrary direction not because influenced by light but because they are negatively geotropic, that is to say, they grow away from the force of gravitation. Plant an acorn or a bulb upside down in the dark and results will be just the same.

In studying insects it was discovered that they too come under the influence of tropisms, and an insect is said to be heliotropic if light is causing forced response, phototropic if artificial light is the compelling influence. Or they may be thermotropic, compelled by heat; chemotropic by chemicals, and so on.

In a normal condition an insect comes under different influences and its normal reactions are to various agents, its behaviour is the result of a balance between them all, but an insect in a tropic condition behaves in a different fashion. We have all seen moths that happen to be phototropic. They will be attracted to an artificial light and unable to leave it. They seem mesmerized, and will either remain facing it or will fly round and round it. If the light is an uncovered flame they will fly into it and perish. The heat of the flame cannot deter them, no other instinct will save them because they are phototropic. Yet on another evening the same moths will not go near a light. They are flying in the same neighbourhood, outwardly the circumstances appear to be exactly the same, yet they are no longer influenced. Some alteration has taken place in the moth itself, it is no longer phototropic.

It is when these tropisms fail, when the normal action does not follow that we learn something about them. The attraction of moths to strong artificial light is a frustration, and we learn what a strong dominant force is causing these distressing casualties.

One of the earliest experiments was carried out on caterpillars. It was discovered that those of some species are heliotropic when they first hatch from the eggs. Their food is half-opened leaf buds which are not there in the autumn when the eggs are laid. The moth finds the right trees instinctively and lays eggs in a sheltered position and there they remain all the winter. They are laid on bark for if they were laid on the leaves when these fell the eggs would be in danger. So the mother insect has done all that is necessary for the next generation, it remains for the brood to find its way to the food quickly. For little fragile things to wander about aimlessly would exhaust them before they had much energy.

So on hatching they are under a tropic influence and are drawn towards the strongest light as surely as the tendril of some plants; they climb upwards towards the tips of branches in the direction where they will find buds. Then when they have reached these the tropism wanes, a chemotropism takes its place from the scent of the buds and the caterpillar feeds.

All this might sound like a fantasy if it were not for the experiments. Some newly hatched caterpillars were put into a glass tube with their food at one end and a strong light at the other. The caterpillars all went to the light end not to the darkened end where their food was. They were not responding normally to the scent from the leaf buds because they were heliotropic. No matter how long they were left there was no change, they remained in the light until they starved although food was in easy reach. This was not an isolated experiment, others had the same result.

The reason for this behaviour appeared to be the failure of the right response to the tropism. This should have been a muscular response, the caterpillars should have started walking upwards. Because the right response did not follow then the controlling force, the tropism could not weaken.

A further discovery was interesting. After caterpillars

had eaten their first meal they were no longer heliotropic, they could find food in a darkened place. The light was still there so that it was in the caterpillars that the change had taken place.

Another early experiment showed that bees were heliotropic when they were about to swarm. A scientist kept a hive of bees in his laboratory on a table under a skylight. It was a glass hive always covered with a dark cloth. When the bees showed signs that they were about to swarm the cloth was taken off the hive in order to see what was happening. Some bees were already coming out through the exit and the rest were on the way, but directly the stronger light shone through from above the bees halted and turned back, making for the top of the hive instead where they remained.

The cloth was put on again and at once the whole community was astir and making for the exit. Again uncovering the top brought all the activities to a standstill. This happened every time. Whenever the cover was off the workers crawled round the inside as near as possible to the light. Finally by leaving the cloth off altogether the swarming ecstasy died down and the bees went about their normal occupations.

It is probable that a great many insects are heliotropic until they are in daylight when they first emerge from the pupa state. Those in underground burrows have to make use of glimmers of light penetrating the surface above them. Insects that have pupated inside wood have likewise only this guide. Before pupating they finish a burrow in a position from which exit is easy, but heliotropism will force them to take the right direction.

A very curious example of what happens when a tropism is frustrated by the wrong response came to my notice some years ago. I had taken members of my boys' club to Epping Forest and we spent the day there on a nature study foray. On the way to the station in the evening we passed through a village and the boys went to look at a stall outside a shop of trinkets and cheap ornaments. Among the china was some very highly scented pottery, vases, bowls and jugs. One of the boys bought a vase and brought it to me to look at because it was full of dead bees. He told me there were quantities of bees lying about on the stall.

I went across to examine them and found that all the pottery ware had corpses of bees in them; there were a few bees still alive, crawling about. The man who owned the stall said that the bees had been a great nuisance. They were coming from hives in a garden not very far away and for the previous six days, ever since the pottery had been put out, these bees were coming to it all day long and stayed on the pottery until they died.

All the wares were arranged in a glass exhibition case which had no back to it. It was about two feet square in front with narrow glass sides. There seemed no possible excuse for all these suicides, but the smaller vases were nearly full of corpses. The front of the case faced the hives so that it might have been thought that the bees would be against the glass. But there were none, they were attracted to the pottery and never left it, the man said.

He thought that it was Indian ware. It had a stronger and more sickly sweet scent than anything I have come across. I can only imagine that the scent might have resembled that of some flowers which the bees visited. In that case they would be in a chemotropic condition.

Neither the homing instinct nor the attraction of light influenced the bees on the scented pottery. They must have perceived the scent from some distance away, and were so gripped by it at close quarters that they were doomed to crawl over and over the scented surface until they died of exhaustion or starvation. And this was in an open case with nothing to hinder them from flying away except a strong scent.

There are several points that illustrate a change of stimulus in directing action in the life history of the fleas which are parasites of sand martins. They live in the nests at the end of long tunnels in sandy banks or cliffs. These burrows are never untenanted. Sand martins return year after year to the same burrow, and as the old ones die the next generation takes their place.

The fleas lay their eggs in the nests and the grubs hatch while the nestlings are being reared. They live on small bits of refuse in the nest and do not bite the young birds. Then when the birds are flown the flea grubs change into pupæ and remain in the deserted burrows.

There are any number of insects which pass the winter as pupæ and when spring comes the increase of temperature affects them and they finish their transformation and come out as mature insects.

It is the change in temperature which controls the stages of their development. With fleas too it is normally heat to which the pupæ respond. What is interesting in the fleas of sand martins is that they do not respond to heat, but have a different agent for their development. So in this very important point they differ from their relatives. Because the burrows are very long— as everybody knows who has taken sand martins' eggs— heat would be an unsatisfactory agent. The temperature at the bottom of the burrows is not greatly affected by sunny days outside which may be warming the sand on the surface.

In their case they are affected by a sudden jar or movement. Pupæ that were brought into a laboratory would not change, the time was past and yet the little cocoons showed no sign of cracking. Then it dawned upon a scientist that it might be the birds themselves which awaken these parasites. So a sharp tap was given to the soil they were resting on. This was successful.

Here is an adaptation to synchronize the final transformation with the return of the birds, their hosts. For, supposing a prolonged winter delayed the sand martins, the fleas would not hatch out too soon because they await the disturbance of the sand on which last year's nestlings were reared.

# 10. Complex Actions

ANYBODY WHO HAS WATCHED ANTS OR wasps carrying out prolonged operations, with meticulous precision which would not discredit human workers, will be quite willing to accept the fact that these insects possess a more highly developed faculty of memory than do the simpler forms of insects.

For the three highest groups—bees, wasps and ants—have peculiar organs, called the mushroom bodies because of their shape, which are near the main nerve centre of the head. As it is only those groups which possess this extra organ and as it is only in these insects that we notice a very superior type of memory, it is considered that the mushroom bodies retain impressions which help to build up an insect's experience.

Another very important point indeed is that these

highly developed insects with superior memory can be taught by experience, and this comes very near to being guided by ideas, though that is an expression which we cannot use for any being which does not possess a mind.

Ants, in particular, have attracted attention from very early days and it used to be taken for granted that these insects must have intelligence, that they could plan for the future, make analogies, think out the best way to do a piece of work. The sage who told us to consider an ant's ways and be wise did not know that he was advising us to be guided by instinct. It was when scientists discovered that no insect possesses anything which compares with the grey matter of the brain that a different attitude was adopted towards the whole subject. Then bit by bit the instincts were studied, and after an immense amount of research insects were discovered to act subconsciously, even when such marvellous achievements were considered as ants' horticulture and dairy farming, and the intricate, exacting work of solitary wasps.

A retentive memory makes the reactions of insects which do not possess it appear very different from those of the three favoured groups. Take for instance a danger common to ants and flies. The latter will return again and again to run exactly the same risks, but the former when impressed by a narrow escape from danger will look for another way out.

## Complex Actions

Several people have recorded that ants will build causeways across fly-papers after a few casualties have occurred. Where ants are troublesome in getting into houses fly-papers have been spread over the window sills to keep them out. It always happens that, when the ants find out by unhappy experiences that these are dangerous, they still will not be deterred but will fetch grit and sand and make safe paths for the workers. Yet at the same time flies will be caught, and having no social instincts will not alter these habits just because there are a lot of fly corpses on the papers. Nor, if they escape are they inclined to keep away, because they do not retain an impression of being partly stuck on the paper and struggling to get free as an ant is able to do through its superior memory.

With the power to retain impressions an insect can build up an image of some locality or object which will help it to return. Wasps and bees can be seen doing this. First a close-up view is taken of their nest or some object which they want to memorize; they will pick out landmarks in the immediate neighbourhood, crawling over them sometimes the better to retain them in memory. Next they will make a map of the spot from a little distance, flying to and fro hovering over anything conspicuous. Finally they circle round from a height with the same objective. When they return they will reverse this process until they locate the spot from which they started. You will not see other insects doing this. Ants are guided by scent mainly and their impressions come through the organ of smell and not their eyes.

The complex actions as they are called are most amazing, both in what is achieved, and also in the way the series of different actions follow on so regularly. There is sometimes an opportunity to watch a long performance. Because of the size of the performers it is not easy to find out exactly what is taking place, but when the chance comes our way it is worth trouble and patience to see it through to a finish.

One little ant drama that I saw in the Society Islands I look back upon with as much pleasure today as when I was an enthralled spectator. It happened on Bora-bora Island where I had been collecting insects for weeks. Every day there had been something new to watch and record, and I had just been thinking that there could not be much more to learn when this fascinating little drama was enacted before my eyes—or under my pocket lens to be exact. I would not for the world have missed it, and for ever afterwards whenever I came across that particular species of ants I used to try to make them stage the same performance.

On my collecting trips from the base camp I was in the habit of sitting down somewhere at midday for a snack, and always put out samples of my lunch on the ground to find out what kind of ants there were in that neighbourhood. On this particular occasion there were five different species running about on the rocks

and bushes but the first visitor who came to inspect my
samples was a blossom beetle. These fly about very
actively in sunlight and feed on open flowers. You can
watch them cramming pollen into their mouths with
both front feet at once—like very greedy children not
well brought up—and sipping nectar. They are always
in a hurry and any movement frightens them. Not only
birds but the blue-tailed skinks and lizards will snap
them up so they are on the look-out for enemies.

That beetle which came to my bait was so happy
with my plum jam that he forgot to be cautious. I
even lifted the piece of bread and jam and watched
him through my pocket lens and that did not disturb
his blissful mood. He was attracted by the bread where
it was soaked with jam; his jaws worked like a pair of
shears. I expect it was exhilarating to discover some
labour-saving food which was like pollen soaked in
nectar so he shaved off minute shreds and extracted
the goodness.

He was frightfully busy absorbing it until the moment
came when he could not eat any more. He walked on
my thumb and meditated awhile and flew away. But
in a couple of minutes he was back again inspecting
the bread and jam from a new angle. It must have
been distressing that he could not start that luxurious
meal all over again. He managed one more tiny sip
of jam then had to admit to himself that he was full

up, there was not room for another drop. So off he flew.

That had been very entertaining, and I looked at the other insect baits feeling that there couldn't be anything more interesting. But there was—the best was to come!

I had set out various samples—a dab of fish paste, a fragment of meat, some crumbs of cake and gingernut, a few flakes of oatmeal, and a spot of toffee which was melting in the sun.

There was a long procession of brown ants carrying off the last of the fish paste. Others were in competition for it, but the brown species had called up some rein-forcements of their soldiers which are much larger than the ordinary workers and have big jaws for chopping. They had chopped up the fish paste and the job was nearly finished. I could see which species had had the lion's share of the fish paste.

Nobody wanted gingernut. One brown worker stag-gered off with a crumb, dropped it, raced round in a panic till she had found it, then in cooler mood decided it wasn't worth carrying. Cake crumbs were going fast but the oatmeal wasn't popular. I had not expected any-body to be interested in that, unless it was a particular species that stores seeds. They might have picked up something if it smelt like grain but they decided that oatmeal wasn't edible.

The melted toffee was a problem. Two kinds of ants were attracted and one red worker got its jaws stuck.

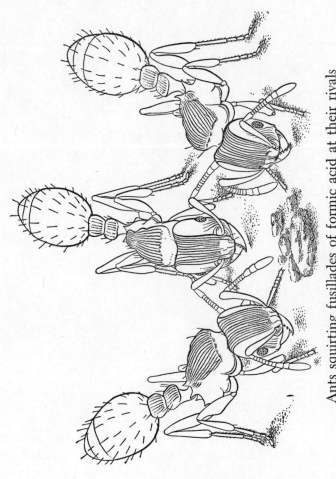

Ants squirting fusillades of formic acid at their rivals

Its mates crowded round but couldn't release it, so finally several got hold of parts of it and pulled backwards, and one ant cut its head off. So that problem was solved to everybody's satisfaction except the headless one's.

Next I looked for the piece of meat, and was very astonished to see it untouched. Several of those species of ants are carnivorous and I had expected that food to be the first to vanish. I examined it through my lens to make sure that it really was the meat, then I noticed a tiny yellow ring round it which was moving and I saw that it was formed by tiny yellow ants. The circle was not quite complete, there were gaps, but workers were hurrying up to fill the gaps.

These ants certainly looked like the small yellow sugar ants, which are such a pest and will get into stored food and make processions across a table where a meal is laid. But I knew already that this was a different race not even nearly related. These ants do not come after sugar, they are carnivorous.

The workers were busy on that morsel of meat already even before the circle was complete, passing through the line of their comrades and fetching bits away. It was all rather mysterious until I realized that the ants of the defensive ring were shooting formic acid at ants belonging to any other species that dared to come near the meat.

Certain ants will do this if their nest is disturbed, these are larger species usually, and if you bend over the nest you will get a strong whiff of formic acid which makes your eyes smart. These yellow ants being so tiny, a jet of formic acid would be infinitesimal, but there was no doubt that it was effective because of the behaviour of other ants trying to snatch the booty.

It was most amusing to watch some of the big bullies who usually got the biggest share in open competition. They would hurry up attracted by the smell of meat and totally unprepared for what awaited them. Then when they were within a certain distance they would receive a volley, and instantly turn round and make off as hard as they could, stopping at intervals to rub parts of their body on one side then the other, twisting themselves into most unwonted attitudes with every sign of discomfort.

Even the fierce red ants, which form nests among leaves and are sometimes called fire ants because of their bite, went through the same undignified contortions. I watched some brown soldiers too blundering along with their chopper jaws gaping ready for the next job, then came the shock of formic acid and they staggered away without making a second attempt.

All this time a thin yellow line of workers was moving between the meat and the nest. When it was all gone the circle broke up and everybody went home.

A most wonderful series of instincts was employed for this elaborate system of defence of food. In the first place the ants which formed the circle had to take a certain position, side by side. Several times I have watched this same species forming their circles, and concluded that each ant took her station at the same distance from the food without regard to the whole circle, and then filled gaps where they found them. There would be many gaps at first.

I never saw one of their own workers hit by mistake. It is possible that being so small they could pass underneath the cloud of formic acid vapour, it seemed however to be fired in short volleys not a continuous stream. The antennæ of the defenders were in movement the whole time, so perhaps the vibration made by the approach of larger ants might have been perceived by those workers. Certainly to an onlooker the aim seemed remarkably accurate.

On one occasion when I was watching, the circle was only half complete when several fire ants succeeded in getting beyond the firing line. They passed through a gap, strode over the tiny ants on their long legs, seized them like a terrier with a rat, bit them and tossed the bodies away. The half-formed circle broke up and the workers scurried away without waiting to pick up their wounded comrades, and the fire ants carried off the booty. That was the one occasion when I knew that encircling manœuvre to fail. The yellow workers had not been quick enough.

In one house that I occupied on Tahiti there was a nest in the ground and the workers had a private road through a crack on to the veranda. Workers of several other kinds of ants were always scavenging in that house. When I was sitting on the veranda I used to kill flies and drop them on the floor to see which ants collected them first. It was significant to see the respect for the tiny fellows if they took up a strategic position. I have seen one worker rout three large fire ants which dared to come near a dead fly. One victim was running round in a circle dragging a hind leg after her as if it were paralysed. Her mates were following to touch her with their antennæ as if puzzled by such crazy behaviour.

Other ants would follow a crowd of the yellow ants carrying off a fly, and when it had been hauled down the crack they would put their heads through the opening and then draw back very hurriedly. I supposed that some of the yellow workers bringing up the rear were having a last shot at them. It is well worth while to keep a lookout for these small entertainers. I assure you they can put up a first-class show.

There is still a great deal to learn about the ants although many people have devoted their lives to the study of them. Some of their histories read like fiction. One of the strangest dramas of all animal life is played by certain ant queens which do not start a colony of their own but invade another kingdom. They deceive the subjects, evade the guard and dispossess the rightful queen. Most of them end by murdering her. It is a most sensational story.

## Complex Actions

The normal proceeding among ants is for a queen when mated to start her own colony unaided. She will find a small chamber—in soil, leaves, or rotten wood according to the habits of the species—lay a few eggs and watch over them until they hatch. It is very usual to find a queen with a small clutch of eggs, guarding and tending them. Or we may find her at the moment the eggs have hatched in a little group of worker ants drying their chitin. She has fed them from special glands all through their larval period and when they emerge her nursing days are over. She will spend her time in laying eggs and they will do the rest.

Such is the normal life of queens but these others which lead the life of an adventuress are quite an exception. They escape the usual drudgery of the first part of their existence by attaching themselves to a flourishing colony of a distinct species. They are known as cuckoo queens. Their manœuvres are startling.

To begin with to gain admittance to an established ants' nest is no easy matter, it is a very delicate and risky procedure. Entrances are well guarded and intruders are recognized at once and slaughtered. The fact that these cuckoo queens usually succeed in gaining access points to their possessing some means of deception. It is thought that their body scent may be like that of the particular ants whose nest they invade, or that they possess some sort of secretion which attracts.

Just as the accepted guests of ants must possess some form of attraction.

Whatever bewitchment is used to deceive the natural guards, in nearly every case the cuckoo queen can pass them. When she is inside she seems to be taken for one of their own queens who has unaccountably been wandering, for the workers will seize her by the antennæ and legs and drag her unresisting to the inner chambers. In like manner they will collect a queen of their own community after her marriage flight.

Having gained that first point in the game and being accepted without being killed she can move about more freely. From time to time she may be challenged but allows herself to be thoroughly examined and their suspicions are allayed. The next manœuvre is bold, for she goes to a heap of eggs and takes a position among them as though they were her own. This act apparently puts the workers quite at ease, they no longer doubt that she is in her rights among them.

Results are not always the same. Sometimes before things reach this point the cuckoo queen is killed. But if she reaches the rightful queen's eggs she will begin to lay her own and the workers will give them the same attention. What is so strange is the behaviour of the rightful queen who is much bigger than the stranger but does not assert herself at all; she does not even try to protect herself when the cuckoo queen, growing arrogant, assaults her. She allows the usurper actually to mount on her back and saw her head off. There is no resistance either on the part of her subjects but perhaps if she took offensive action they might support her. This nobody can say, for the entire drama results from hereditary instincts, and no ant seems to have the power to call the bluff of the cuckoo queen when she is once accepted, though her life might end suddenly at almost any point of her strange career.

There has been another very interesting development among some large red ants which are detested wherever they are found—in Queensland, New Guinea, India and elsewhere—because of their tiresome habit of setting up homes between leaves, and their fierce resentment if disturbed.

The bite is very painful and to have a shower of these ants fall on you when trying to pick a flower or a leaf is an experience not easily forgotten. Small independent communities are formed in small nests between two or three leaves woven together at the edges.

The ants have to keep careful watch over their flimsy structures for leaves of soft texture are chosen and are often damaged by something falling against them or by wind. Perhaps this makes the ants extra watchful, for a touch will cause a sally of furious defenders which take a position on the top of the nest with widely distended jaws. Not only do they take up this hostile attitude but they will mark the position of the assumed enemy, run down the trunk of the tree and race to the attack.

At that juncture it is wise to beat a retreat. Cattle very soon learn to run for safety. The ants hold on so tenaciously that you may have to pull their heads off and deal with those separately before you can unlock the mandibles.

Trees and bushes in a favourable position will be taken over and covered with nests. I have counted 42 on a small hibiscus tree 8 feet high. Every available large leaf seemed to have been utilized.

So these red ants are very well known where they occur but few people are aware of the most unusual and interesting habits connected with the business of building these nests. The edges of the leaves are drawn together with silk to form a globular chamber. But ants do not possess silk glands and it was puzzling to know how they could do this expert piece of weaving. There are several exits but between them is a network of silk strands crossed several times. Entomologists puzzled over this for years. It was even suggested that the ants might collect spiders' gossamer for the purpose. There was no doubt that if ants discovered that they could utilize gossamer they would set about collecting it but how could they make it stick to the leaves? The threads harden directly they are in contact with the air.

It remained a mystery until two entomologists discovered the answer independently at about the same time. The true explanation sounded so fantastic that both confessed afterwards that they hesitated to put it forward, and it was received with a good deal of scepticism.

For the answer is that the workers bring from the nurseries their own larvæ at the stage when they are about to pupate, and hold them up to the edge of the leaves while workers with their mandibles keep the margins in position. The larvæ produce a small quantity of silk to make their own cocoons and have a little to spare. It is a very sketchy cocoon certainly, but the workers must be able to gauge exactly how long to hold up these living shuttles. Guided by instinct the larvæ mechanically weave to and fro and the workers keep them held against the leaves until each has woven a little patch. Then they are taken back to the nursery and allowed to complete their own cocoons.

The whole amazing operation raises many questions. How did the first ant happen upon this ingenious utilization of a glandular secretion which they did not themselves possess? Can it have occurred accidentally in the first place? But even so it would have to be universally adopted before it could become a fixed habit. These questions are eternally cropping up whenever we have anything to do with living insects.

Near one of my inland camps in New Guinea I happened to come across one of their nests which had been damaged, possibly by a gale. The sides were gaping and six workers had been assigned the very difficult task of holding the edges of two leaves together with their mandibles.

They were clinging to the surface of a leaf on one side with two pairs of legs, the claws gripping firmly, and they held the other leaf edge with their forelegs and strong jaws. It looked a very strained position and made one's own jaws ache in sympathy. But this was an exceptional opportunity to see as much as possible of the operation. I made a preliminary sketch of the six workers and the two gaps which would have to be filled in with silk. Hitherto I had only been able sometimes to make out an ant's head on the inside of the nest moving to and fro and was never sure whether it was actually holding up a larva. This time I hoped for a chance to see more but did not after all. What I did see however was quite interesting.

Every day I visited that nest and made comparisons with my sketch. It was astonishing to find on the third morning that the original six had not shifted their positions. Since one cannot imagine that they were working in shifts and being replaced at intervals by other workers those ants must have remained in that very unrestful pose for at least 78 hours. I noticed a movement from inside several times while watching. Workers were coming up to the gap and touching the martyrs with their antennæ. They may have been ministering to their hunger by injecting a drop or two. One hopes so, it seems a long time to remain in that tense attitude. I considered that the accident when the leaves gaped must have occurred at an unfortunate time when there were no larvæ in the nurseries at that stage when they could be called upon for house repairs.

Instincts for carrying out work of this description involve such fineness of perception, such exactness of treatment and delicate adjustment as to leave one bewildered. How did it begin? How were the first individuals of that particular race directed to make use of the only available material that could be used to interlace leaves? The instincts to collect certain materials and make use of them—leaves, clay, bits of bark and moss—do not fall into the same category. If ants collected their progeny's silk and carried it away this would be useless for the purpose. It must be used at exactly the moment when it issues from the mouth before it is dry and has lost its adhesive quality. Hence the haste with which the larvæ are hustled out of their serried ranks at exactly the right moment. But what informs the workers of this moment?

The success in exploiting any new area for food can be noticed times without number, and the cause of that success can be guessed. For everywhere are the workers parcelling the ground among them and thoroughly exploring soil, vegetation, rocks for edible debris, dead or injured insects, living insects and corpses. Should a worker laden with booty arrive at the nest it is instantly inspected by others and they start off on its trail at once, and search the locality. If unsuccessful they must return empty, if only part of the booty has been collected they finish the job, surrounding it in numbers, driving away competitors until every scrap has been collected. One imagines the same manœuvre takes place when a fresh locality is discovered.

A river near one of my camps in New Guinea provided a very good hunting site for myself and I made daily trips along the banks. There had been three days without rain and the river bed shrank to shallow fordable strips with a chain of deep pools. But one morning it was evident that the water had subsided in the night, and I walked on the dry bed to what had been an islet in the mid current to find that it was no longer cut off from the bank. The evening before at six o'clock when I left it the water had to be waded through, but by now it was a thin trickle. In that short period since daylight the red ants had discovered new territory to exploit. They were running over the rocks in zig-zagging trails to avoid the water, crossing a fallen branch and exploring the islet. And in one small bush about four feet high with soft young leaves there were a couple of nests being made already. The weaving was in progress which means that larvæ from some of the numerous communities of the bank must have been carried over to perform the interlacing.

As another example of work of a very complex character making demands upon all the faculties of an insect I must quote the duels which take place between the largest of the hunter wasps and large spiders, a very thrilling scene for those who have the luck to watch it.

If it should be a fight to a finish then it is a toss-up which will be the winner because the duellists are so well matched. Hunter wasps are specially equipped for dealing with a prey which is cunning and strong, but both of them have poisonous weapons so the parry and thrust may go on for a very long time. There are swift moves and counter-moves until at last the opportunity comes to one or other of them for the final blow.

I have been able to observe some scenes in this drama very often but seldom had a chance to see the opening phases of the combat. Only once have I had a good view at close quarters when I could actually watch each action. On that occasion by the merest stroke of good luck I was witness of the finish as well which was quite unpredictable. The whole drama was simply enthralling, the opponents changing their position or their tactics every few seconds.

It happened in New Guinea. As I was walking through rather thick brushwood a large hairy spider ran in front of me. It was of the kind which is popularly called a bird-eating spider—and sometimes erroneously a tarantula. This was a female, males are much smaller.

It surprised me, but not because these spiders were rare in that district for as it happened I had been collecting some the day before. They live in holes in a bank and I had dug out five and taken them in a net without getting bitten. No, it wasn't surprising to see this spider but the fact that it was running about in broad daylight was unusual, for they are nocturnal. This needed explanation.

Many a time have I seen them coming out of their holes at dusk; they first take a prolonged drink from damp leaves and moss, then run about searching for large cockroaches, crickets, small mammals and other prey. I have found one feeding on a night-lizard, a gecko. They do occasionally attack tiny nestlings.

It struck me at once that this spider which crossed my path must have been disturbed by something, but it was not I who had disturbed her. From time to time the burrow is outgrown and a new one must be dug, she might have been turned out from a temporary lodging, but by what? I waited and watched.

In a few seconds a large purple-black wasp appeared, evidently on the spider's trail for she flew low over the ground on a zig-zag course, examining objects from time to time for any sign of life. No movement could have escaped her keen eyes.

Something more than eyesight guided her, of course, it must have been sense of smell as well, for after following the direction which the spider had taken she dropped to the ground, and crawled under the log at the exact spot where the spider had entered a hollow.

## Complex Actions

As she disappeared the spider shot out from the opposite side and ran up a tree nearby, got into a crook of a bough and appeared to melt into shadow. An ordinary mortal like myself could not separate it from the background. The wasp reappeared after a minute's search, but before she went on with the chase she flew upwards. For a minute I believed she had lost the trail, but she hadn't, she must have known that the trail was pretty hot just there. She was only taking wider bearings of the locality with its chief landmarks. Wasps do this at intervals, and with their extraordinary powers for memorizing they can retain an image of their surroundings so that they are not lost.

After making a large-scale map of the country around she came lower and memorized objects near the ground—myself included. Then she made a more minute inspection, picked up the scent at once and the hunt was on again.

The stage was now a small glade made by a big tree that had fallen bringing down others which had been guyed up by innumerable ropes attached to their big neighbour. The magnificent head of the tree that had formerly been in the clouds was lying near me. Over the ground were scattered quantities of lovely little orchids and ferns which love to be aloft wreathed in mists. Large logs splintered off the tree's giant limbs lay around.

A small tree that had escaped the general destruction now harboured the spider. Very cautiously I moved round it to the farther side to watch. Sudden movements might have frightened either of the combatants at this stage, later the struggle became so intense at close quarters that their attention was fully absorbed.

I marked where the spider had melted into its background and saw its tireless enemy follow exactly where it had run up the trunk. Then she probably saw it for she dropped suddenly. But as she pounced the spider ran over the branch and down the trunk. I caught sight of it as it sped across the clearing to the log where I had first seen it take refuge.

The wasp was aware that she had missed, but was not likely to give up at that stage. Again she flew up into the air and circled around taking her bearings anew. Now they included fresh landmarks which she inspected flying near and hovering in front of them. I was not included in the new series.

She drove the spider from under the log in a few moments, then it bolted into a hollow in a mossy stump near the ground. I crawled up to it on all fours. It was a little shallow cavern and did not seem to have a bolt hole so I rightly concluded that this was where the final scenes were to take place. The wasp dropped to the ground and ran to and fro excitedly looking for clues, and I lay flat taking a position from which I could see the spider. The hollow was probably only a little wider than the spider's own burrow, all the advantage is with the spider when she is at home. The burrows are not deep and they dip at the end of the first passage; the spider sits at a lower level, its jaws ready for the first intruder, prey or foe.

This spider had a fine strategic position which would challenge all the wasp's cunning. I could see that she was in fighting attitude. A spider's vulnerable part is its soft abdomen, and this the wasp attacks trying to place a sting where it can paralyse a nerve centre. This wasp was trying to get underneath the spider or pass along its side, and at the same time avoid the mandibles which can strike with incredible swiftness. I should have liked to see every detail but even with my face near the ground I could only see the movements. The wasp would make a dart. The spider, with the armoured forepart of the body upraised protecting its hinder part, barred the way and tried to strike downwards. The wasp retired and made a fresh attempt on the other side, which was again frustrated.

This manœuvre was repeated I do not know how many times. Suddenly I was aware of the climax, for the spider had its abdomen towards me and was slowly backing out of the hollow, moving only the legs on the left side while those on the right were dragged over the ground for she was half paralysed.

Then there was a mix-up at the mouth of the hollow and I expected soon to see the wasp begin to lever out the large flabby carcase, which was an operation I particularly wanted to observe. But the end was not yet. I judged afterwards that the wasp must have miscalculated and considered life to be extinct before the spider was really helpless. Only two legs were quivering and the rest showed no movement when the wasp crawled out but it was evident at once that she herself was in distress.

She tried hard to clean her antennæ, always the first movement of an insect when things go wrong, to sharpen its wits ready for action. But this time it had no effect for she too was partly paralysed. Even that instinctive movement was unfinished. She just managed to rise from the ground but when attempting to settle on a twig she missed it and fell. Again there was an effort to clean her antennæ, a feeble effort for she was getting rapidly weaker. When she took off again she rose no higher than a couple of feet, collided with a trunk and flew unsteadily in a lopsided manner at a sloping angle which landed her in some moss. When I picked her up she was quite dead.

Then I went back to the spider which had been feebly trying to get back into the hollow on two legs. It lay still in the entrance and when I pulled it out it was dead too. So each opponent had succeeded in

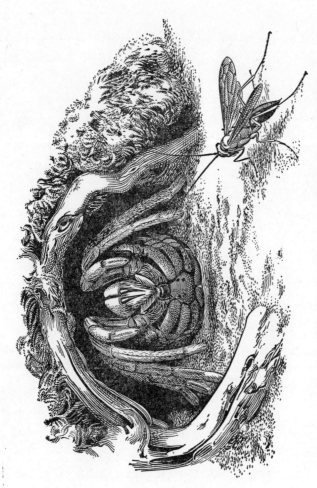

The wasp made a fresh onslaught from the other side

dealing a well placed stroke with its poisoned weapon and as a result both had succumbed.

These are only a few of the examples which could be quoted of the achievements of insects through hereditary instincts with a latitude allowed for changing their tactics to suit circumstances.

Is it surprising that our ancestors attributed to some insects the faculty of a human mind?

# 11. Individual Actions

THERE IS A PARTICULAR TYPE OF ACTIONS which personally I always consider of outstanding interest—those performed by an individual insect which differ from normal behaviour of its race. It is not often that we have the chance of noticing them but that makes the favourable moment all the more valuable. No matter how slight the variation from hereditary instinctive actions it is always well worth recording; it shows us what an insect is capable of doing just as a structural abnormality shows what it is capable of producing on its own body.

Among the simple primitive forms this does not occur but the three most highly developed groups—ants, bees and wasps—give many examples of individual actions. We meet with them chiefly among the first and last of these more often than among the bees. Perhaps this is because their experiences are more varied, or perhaps because most of the ants and wasps are carnivorous and hunt for living prey which keep them always on the alert. Bees have quite a variety of tasks to perform but they are vegetarians and their outside activities are concerned with the vegetable world so we should expect their behaviour to be more stereotyped.

It is always a surprise when these instances of individual behaviour come to our notice. We are so accustomed to each phase in these insects' lives that we are inclined to doubt our own interpretation of anything unusual, but as a matter of fact the more one watches their work the more one is struck by the fact that it is seldom carried out in exactly the same manner every time. So often a little hitch occurs, something in the usual chain of events fails, then you may see the insects changing their tactics and making trials until something succeeds. This is most absorbing to watch. The astonishing fact about ants in such a dilemma is that usually they hit upon what may be the only solution to their problem in such a short time. This is generally the work of an individual leader and the community will follow and complete the task.

One potter wasp among a group that were building on the same veranda performed such a very sagacious act that it was a thousand pities she could not pass on to the next generation a new habit for dealing with an emergency.

Potter wasps, although not social, are likely to choose the same site for making their nests because they need the same conditions which are a good surface for building upon and shelter from rain. So a score or more will be working within a few inches of one another. They have a very amiable nature, there may be a few scuffles but they never fight with stings, it is more often a bumping match. But there is no sort of communal work, each female builds her own nest unaided.

About a dozen potters were building cells under the veranda of a house when I stayed on an island of the New Hebrides. There are few entertainments so engrossing as watching these wasps at work. One never tires of it. For from the beginning when they select a site for the first of the cluster of cells until they seal up the last one, the wasps are following out a long series of events for which they have evolved a long series of instincts. The work requires entirely different instincts at different junctures. There are four series. First comes the moulding of clay, next a hunt for living prey with which to stock the little urn-shaped cells, then the egg-laying business and afterwards a return to the moulding in order to close the cell.

So the change over from one series of instincts to the next is from one job to something of quite another type. When one job is finished a fresh nerve impulse

starts off the next series. And this is without the faculty
of mind. The wasp does not think, "Now this job is
over I must concentrate on the next." By hereditary
instinct one series gives impulse to the next in sequence.

My potters were having a difficult time because conditions were very dry. No rain had fallen for over a
week, and those light showers which before that had
blessed the country at night had not even penetrated
the surface of the ground. No heavy rain had given it
a soaking for six weeks. One saw the result in the potters'
work. Not only were they hard put to it to find moist
mud when all their familiar pools and puddles were dry
with cracks gaping, but the clay they did find would not
remain stuck on the wooden walls which were unusually
hot and dry.

That I considered was the reason why there were
several single cells and some had been deserted when
half finished. The potters were not satisfied that they
made a firm enough foundation for others. There were
little dabs of clay too which had been forsaken after
the first load had been plastered on the wall. One could
see that there were already cracks showing. They were
not safe foundations for a cluster of four or five cells.

One wasp had started a cell on the stout wire wash-
ing-line near the back premises. Wet laundry had been
hung on it and this seemed promising; so a hopeful
potter began operations in the humid neighbourhood
of one of my bush suits. She had only half completed

it when the clothes were dry, and the pretty little cell was twanged off the wire when the native laundress took away the suit to iron it.

I watched the potter examining the wreck. It must have been a very puzzling catastrophe, but after hovering over the spot with a fresh load of clay and walking along the wire on each side she abandoned that site.

There is no time wasted but the potters do not hurry, all their actions are very deliberate. One could imagine that they were planning the next step in advance. Yet it is marvellous what is accomplished in the end.

The antennæ come into play all the time, these very sensitive organs with the mouth palps as well are testing and measuring every detail. The antennæ give such expression as the potter bends over her absorbing work; they make her appear absorbed or puzzled, hesitating or determined. If she is agitated over anything they quiver with excitement.

Every load of clay seems to be about the same size but some may be heavier because very often there is considerable embarrassment over landing it safely. A laden wasp may be overburdened and have to retire to adjust the load or discard a fragment. It carries out a process of kneading and welding at the place where the clay is collected. Some of the wasp's saliva is mixed with it but it seems all-important that the clay should be suitably moist in the beginning before being worked to the right consistency. When that part of the proceed-

Potter wasp moulding her urn

ings is satisfactory the wasp rolls it into a ball, and flies off with it carried between the forelegs and the horny plate which is her upper lip. When she has settled with the load near her nest or on it the wasp clings with four legs and uses the front pair to guide the new load. So we realize how very necessary it is to have six legs when making pottery upon a vertical surface.

Now the ball is placed in position and it can be seen that the horny upper lip is a tool like a mason's trowel; it is pressed against the soft clay and the ball is unrolled backwards in a ribbon-like strip with one deft movement. The wasp's legs hold it while she presses it into position obliquely on her little urn. Those oblique lines which are plainly visible when the pottery is dry signify the different loads which slightly overlap, but the potter spends some time in smoothing the structure so there is no visible join. They are pretty, those oblique lines, they give a pattern.

When the urn has reached the required size it is finished off at the top with a neck and lip. Such great pains are taken over this part. Over and over again the potter walks round it, applying her little trowel till the lip is exactly symmetrical. Then she flies away for provisions to stock the cell.

These wasps that I was watching stock their cells with caterpillars. Those belonging to another group use spiders. The search and hunt are carried out by the next series of instincts which have an utterly different objective. The quest being caterpillars the potter will have no interest in clay for the time being. During the hunt she may be near an ideal collecting place for clay but it will not even be observed, all her faculties are needed for the hunting. Those that hunt spiders have perhaps a more active time, but my wasps had to master the camouflage of the particular kind of caterpillars she needed. They were small and green and very difficult to distinguish from the foliage of the plants they fed on. The potters had to examine each leaf and test it with the antennæ moving all the time.

An immensely important matter to her is to carry in memory an image of the place where her nest is situated. Before leaving it the potter makes sure of recognizing the site. She will first walk round it touching the wall, then will examine any object near, a nail, peeling bark, or a crack in the weather-boarding. Next she hovers within a certain distance noting other landmarks. Then you will see her flying in circles above the house before the hunt for caterpillars begins.

For these hunts may take the potter to some distance. It is a very absorbing game, but when it is over she must remember how to return by picking up her landmarks. When she switches over to the pottery work again she may be near a plant with caterpillars while collecting the clay but will not observe them. And each locality, her nest, clay pits and hunting ground are separate images to be called up for each section of her task.

In the neighbourhood to which I have been referring only one accessible piece of water, a rather deep pool, remained at the end of that dry spell. I noticed that wasps were forsaking the veranda and building on a tree trunk not far from the pool which I had not seen them using before. It made a better foundation than the dry timber of the house. But one potter remained. She was building on a wire-netting basket slung near the roof out of reach of the rats, her clay was partly on the potatoes in the basket. I wondered whether that site was cooler or whether the cells were less likely to crack at a horizontal angle than they would on the face of the wall. I watched that individual potter very carefully.

Halfway across from the pool she would stop with her load of clay at a dripping tap just outside the house. It struck me that she seemed to require a great many drips—she seemed more thirsty than her comrades—so I sat down by the tap for a near view. She was not drinking as I had supposed but was carrying each load of clay under the tap and mixing it with the few drops of water that collected on a narrow ledge before it soaked through.

One may guess that this wasp had memorized that spot for getting a passing drink. But the interesting point is that she was making unusual visits, for she collected the clay at the pool where all the other wasps were scooping it up but brought her load because it was too dry for her purpose to another place which was associated in memory with water.

It was not a merely mechanical action for she would then have continued to build and let her cells crack as the others were doing. It was an association of experiences and failure in her normal task which prompted a new and extraordinarily successful experiment. Yet it was an individual action. Not one of the rest tackled the problem in the same way nor did they copy her.

A still more unexpected action I saw performed by a potter wasp belonging to another group—one which preys on spiders. This time there were scores of nests being built underneath the high platform of a bungalow. To watch them at work I had a short ladder and sat on the top rung which gave a perfect view. Being so near the wasps I was unfortunately selected as a landmark. When I left my post I saw one distracted wasp circling for a long time because there was something wrong with her map. I believe they depend entirely on landmarks and if these cannot be picked out accurately will forsake the nest and start from zero once more rather than risk working on the wrong site.

The wasp which gave me such a surprise by her behaviour was one of that mob. I wanted to test her memory and see whether she would notice any alteration in her nest. So while she was absent fetching clay I got a twig and rammed it through the wall of a half finished cell. She noticed it at once although it was not on the side that she was working at. She deposited her load, walked over the cell several times touching the twig each time with her antennæ then finished welding in her last load. After this she had another inspection and was busy with her mandibles on the spot then flew away. She had bitten off the twig and smoothed clay over the place.

So far her sequence of instincts had not been disturbed. She had discovered the interference with her cell, had remedied it as far as possible and continued her work at the point where it had been interrupted.

After all, what I had done was not an abnormal occurrence, a twig might fall on the cells and become embedded in the clay although this was not a likelihood. So my next interference was calculated to be unusual. I took a brass drawing pin and pressed it into the clay as far as the head. The potter had certainly never come across a drawing pin, her hereditary instincts could not be expected to guide her behaviour when confronted with such a novelty. I watched keenly.

On this occasion the potter certainly showed agitation. She realized at once that the nest had been tampered with, dropped the ball of clay and did a sort of war dance on the nest vibrating her wings with a loud buzzing. She ran about on it for some time, then her energy seemed to flag and she remained quite motionless except for the antennæ. It was the next action which was so astonishing. There was a wall near, on which was a patch of bright sunlight that had attracted a number of flies. The potter without any provocation on their part flew to the patch and drove them all away. She returned to her nest but when all came back to continue sunning themselves she did this a second time.

Apparently I was not under suspicion. I was very near and she had examined my face several times before leaving the nest so I was accepted as part of the surroundings. But the interference with her nest was fastened upon the innocent flies.

Much uneasiness is always shown by solitary bees and wasps if anything moves near the nest. I have seen snails, beetles, centipedes and spiders attacked. So the behaviour of this wasp towards the flies was in itself a natural action, but she connected them with that drawing pin. They were several feet away and they had been flying about and resettling the whole of the time that I had been watching, and the potter up to then had taken no notice of them. There was indeed no reason for her to do so. It seems that when roused by something very unusual in her clay cell she had pounced upon them as the most probable offenders.

This last interference proved too much for her. No attempt was made to do any more to the nest. She forsook it. This was a pity because I should have liked to keep her in view and watch whether her late harrowing experience had put her out in the sequence of normal events. But in that large number of potters this was impossible. What happened most probably was that she would take a rest and perhaps sip some nectar, then start all over again.

It is amusing to test wasps' memory. Experiments have been made to baffle the recognition of nests by the social wasps by putting something conspicuous near the entrance, then, when they had accustomed themselves to look for it, the landmark was removed. First something red was placed in position and all the returning workers would hover over that as a useful landmark. When it was taken away they were confused and took some time to find their entrance, but it was noticed that they picked out red leaves and examined the ground near them before finally recognizing the right place.

All kinds of colour tests have been made with wasps and bees. In both groups there is good eyesight and a retentive colour memory as in the bumble bee which after being busy with sunflowers was seen to make a close inspection of the yellow breast of a parrot. It was indeed to human eyes exactly the same colour. It proved that in that case the bee was not relying on its sense of smell but only on sight.

Another individual action which was most curious was performed by a leaf-cutting bee, a black bee which was very common on one island and there was no other species there which at all resembled it. It makes burrows in dry posts but does not line them with leaves as some near relatives do. So when I noticed one of these bees carrying, as I thought, a piece of yellow leaf, I gave chase and caught it to make sure that it was actually the familiar black bee. It dropped its load inside the net and to my astonishment it was not a leaf but a ball of pollen.

These bees collect pollen but not in that manner. They hold it on the underside of the body where there are rows of very stiff bristles for that purpose, the scopa. The bees push the pollen on to this with the front legs. But this individual was carrying a ball of it as a potter wasp does, lodged between the chin and the forelegs. I watched carefully after that and never saw other bees behaving in this odd fashion. Hundreds of times I have seen the same bees on other islands but only carrying pollen as they should.

It would be most interesting to know what stimulus prompted that change of habit which required the exercise of quite a different set of muscles. There may have been a superabundance of pollen but if so it influenced that bee quite differently from others of the same race.

On that same island three wasps got into the habit of visiting me every morning. They arrived with my coffee and at once began a tour of inspection of the breakfast table. They were all solitary wasps, three inquisitive ladies of very modest dimensions, about as long as my thumb-nail. Handsome creatures with patches of silky golden hair which caught the light as they ran about. They were models of neatness and withal very decorative.

The first search was for granulated sugar. I put the bowl in a different place every morning but they would soon find it, then settle down for a meal. They do not crush the granules but take up one at a time, turn it round and round between their jaws sucking it, then drop that and take another. I had to stop this performance because it took so long that I had scarcely a chance to serve myself. I put out a few granules on the table for them and then used lump sugar for my coffee. That baffled them, they couldn't lick much from the big lumps so left them alone.

The milk was the most alluring game, they were very fond of milk. Nothing would keep them away from that white milk jug, and being greedy and always in a desperate hurry they were constantly falling in. I got quite tired of rescuing them. Every morning I used to put the jug in a different place but after a short search they always found it. You can't hide much from a hunting wasp. Then I poured the milk into a blue jug and covered the white one with newspapers. That puzzled them. Sadly they hunted all over the veranda until they had located the white jug under the papers, and explored it outside and in to make sure it was dry. Then one wasp discovered milk in the blue jug and the two others followed her. Again my meal had to be postponed while I fished wasps out of the milk, so finally I covered the top with muslin until I could finish my breakfast and give them their morning's rations.

The most enterprising wasp of the three wouldn't be put off in this manner. She found a small hole in the muslin which she enlarged until she could get her head through. Then she stuck—and panicked. I had a hectic time getting her free without breaking her neck, which in an insect is a very flimsy affair. All the time I had to avoid being stung, for she seemed certain that an enemy was trying to trap her. Her long sting on the end of a very mobile body was being thrust in every direction to jab at my fingers, which added to the liveliness of the struggle.

After this my milk was served in a jug with a metal lid, and an extra plate was laid on my table. Before I poured out my coffee a few drops of milk were put into the plate for the wasps. They soon found it and all three sat sipping away luxuriously. You could see the drops rapidly diminishing. Then they flew away—heavily after such a big feed.

I was very curious to see whether they would remember or would have to re-learn their lesson next day. One wasp flew to the plate at once, the other two wasted time in going through the same manœuvres as the day before, first hunting out the white jug then the blue jug and examining both very thoroughly before they came to the plate. But they remembered after this and would settle on their plate without delay, or even hunt for it if I put it in a different place.

I had no series of different coloured plates or I could have experimented with them. For these wasps can memorize colours like the bees and the social wasps, and it is interesting to test their ability. Those particular hunting wasps have a lot of memorizing to do while performing their daily tasks. One may meet them in the woods dragging a dead cricket to a hole. They dig the hole first for its reception. It is wonderful that they can remember where they put it—you might think that the excitement of a hunt would put such things out of their head. Then they will remember the spot where the cricket was found and go back for another. Like other wasps they have certain landmarks to guide them so these have to be memorized too. They will examine them whenever they return to make sure it is the right locality. So actually these wasps must have some sort of mental pictures at all the different stages of their complicated work. The visit to my breakfast table must have been a pleasant interlude in their duties. When the cricket is safely buried, an egg is laid on it and the burrow is closed. So there is a store of provisions ready for the wasp grub when it hatches out of the egg.

So these three wasps too had *normal* instinctive actions, but the discovery of the sugar and milk on my table led to new temporary habits at the same time every morning, while their near relatives were carrying out their usual tasks without any diversion.

The timber of that rest house was very dry and being thatched with coconut fronds, the roof accommodated many guests, especially geckos and large beetles. Myriads of very small beetles were coming out of the piles and the doorposts where they had been feeding inside the wood for a couple of years or so. Now was their time to emerge. They left very neat round exit holes leading to their empty burrows and these exactly fitted the requirements of some smaller wasps who were very busy utilizing them for their own nests. These too were solitary wasps. They have no queens or workers, the female does all the work unaided. These were jet black with an elegant pattern of yellow dots like buttons.

The work is terribly strenuous and exacting and it keeps a wasp very busy throughout daylight hours. She first makes a thorough inspection of the burrow and tidies it. Any little bit of sawdust scattered while the grub was gnawing the wood is brought out and thrown away. Then when the wasp is satisfied that the walls are smooth and everything in order she starts work. The burrow is exactly her size, she can step in and out quite easily. That is why this particular species appropriates the empty burrows of those particular beetles when they have quitted. The wasp now starts hunting for small caterpillars. You may watch her crawling over low growing plants, examining every leaf and stem methodically until she locates a caterpillar. If it isn't quick enough to drop off the plant and hide she seizes it, stings it till it goes limp and then flies with it to the burrow which she has chosen.

Now she carries out what is really an expert engineering feat. She has one end of the caterpillar gripped firmly in her jaws and pressed between her front legs, but the rest is dangling and she has to engineer it bit by bit through the narrow opening of the burrow. It is as if you held between your teeth a badly stuffed bolster sagging at one end, and had to manœuvre it into a drainpipe in the middle of a wall. Yet the wasp manages to achieve this several times a day, pushing it in bit by bit until it is safely inside, then she slips in herself and pulls from the back until it is in the right place. Then she goes to hunt for another caterpillar. About six little caterpillars altogether make up her quota, then an egg is laid on the last one and the hole is sealed with a little fine gravel.

There were many of these wasps in the house engaged on this task. One was exactly over my table where I packed specimens and wrote up my notes. She was rather a nuisance especially at the end of the day. For if it is not the moment to seal the burrow by late afternoon, the wasp will sit just inside and do sentry-go in case there are enemies about who might steal her store of caterpillars. There is a serious risk of ants finding them for they would soon cart them away. And there are parasites which might nip in and lay an egg there, then the parasite grub would eat the caterpillars or else the wasp grub. So there is a real danger to guard against.

But if I were at my table any hasty movement would make the wasp rush out and sting me. It's only a slight sting but it is tiresome to be taken for an enemy and I used to revenge myself by teasing the wasp. Her tiny head was just visible in the hole, twisting from side to side to watch for any movement. So I used to make my pair of forceps crawl up the post, tapping the wood as it came and behaving as though it were a monster hunting for the nests of little black wasps.

Directly the tapping began out would pop a head and wait for the forceps to come within reach. Then she attacked it fiercely, biting the steel with her tiny mandibles. When the forceps remained still she seemed satisfied that the enemy was slain and would return to the burrow, rushing in head foremost as was her habit. Directly she turned her back to do this I would give her a little tap. Now what is interesting is that such habits are hereditary. That particular species always enters her burrow head first, others always enter backwards. All over the house you could see these little wasps going into the burrows head-first, but that particular wasp after several times having a tap from the forceps wouldn't turn her back again. She lowered herself very cautiously backwards into the burrow, keeping a bright look-out for this treacherous enemy which pretended to be dead and then came to life again when she was not looking. It is an interesting point, because it proves once more that some insects are not completely hide-bound by their instincts, but that individuals can change a hereditary habit on occasions.

A truly fascinating book *Wasps, Social and Solitary* was written years ago about these highly developed groups, the social and the solitary wasps, by two American naturalists, George and Elizabeth Peckham. They spent days in studying wasps in their neighbourhood. They studied not only the specific labours but the specific manner of carrying out each section. They learnt to know individuals and found several instances where behaviour differed according to moods and perhaps temperaments.

It is one of the best books on insects ever written because the authors followed the wasps for long distances and were able thus to time the actions, measure the ground covered, and observe small points which had never before been recorded.

The Peckhams first noted that some wasps seem much neater and more methodical over making nests. That is noticeable directly one becomes interested in a particular species and can compare the ways of the females. Among diggers it is not only the nature of the soil that they are working in, which accounts for individual ways of tackling the task but some wasps are hurried and satisfied more easily with results. Others are fastidious in observing niceties, they will return again and again to smooth an entrance, rearrange particles of soil. The cause may be physical. The moment for laying the egg may be approaching and the arduous work of preparation may have been delayed. There is a distressing incident in the Peckhams' book when an egg protruded before the agitated wasp had completed the first part of her work. Something had set the internal machinery in motion a little too soon. This is another reminder of how precisely events must synchronize.

One totally unexpected result from the Peckhams' work was the discovery that one of the most attractive diggers, elegant with slender waist and long legs and very active, was actually using a tool for putting finishing touches to her burrow.

Many people must have watched members of this group carrying caterpillars which seem far too large for an insect of such size. Many people may have watched the operation of digging a burrow to receive the prey. But not everybody would realize what a tremendous feat is accomplished, the tests of memory, of strength, of endurance involved.

When mating is over the wasp starts work at once. She first finds a suitable place for digging a burrow and then memorizes the exact spot—she will spend a good deal of time over this for so much depends upon it.

Next she hunts for a suitable caterpillar. These hunts take a very long time. You may watch the same wasp examining every part of a plant then passing disappointed to the next but it is seldom that one witnesses the capture. For in this species only one caterpillar is used to provision a nest, so it is essential to find something large enough or the wasp larva will be on short rations.

When the wasp is laden after stinging the caterpillar into quiescence it is no mean achievement to fly with it to the burrow. It is carried under the wasp's body gripped tightly with all her legs so that the weight is correctly distributed, but with all this care the flight is wobbly and often a wasp must settle to readjust her load.

One would imagine her attention is distracted yet she is successfully carrying in memory the direction to her burrow and all the landmarks chosen to guide her to it. She arrives on the spot and locates the hole. It is all the more difficult to do so because the wasp covers the entrance before leaving it. Why this is done is not obvious, it would not take much time to turn out any trespasser which might enjoy a fat caterpillar that it had not been obliged to hunt. But anyhow, this is a habit of that species of digger wasps.

So the wasp drags in the caterpillar, backing into

the burrow herself then levering it slowly into position, comes out again and with great care covers it in and rearranges the disturbed soil to leave no trace of the opening.

This we can understand is very necessary. There are so many carnivorous creatures that might discover this food store and undo all her work. But when the Peckhams saw a wasp, which they had been following through all the phases of her work, pick up a pebble and pound down the loose soil on the hidden entrance they could hardly believe their eyes. This is indeed an action which is very far removed from automatic response to stimuli. It is analogous to the ants' use of silk produced by their larvæ to weave the leaves of their home together. The Peckhams lay on the ground, to bring their eyes as close as possible to the wasp's head and watch exactly what was taking place. They had to see it several times before being sure they were not mistaken, because it was such a revolutionary idea that an insect could make use of a tool. But these two witnesses were able to record the habit and confirm it by the observations of others.

The struggle with a caterpillar is not a light affair. The wasp has to get her sting placed in a nerve centre which controls muscular movement, and the caterpillar by twisting and rolling very rapidly makes this operation far more difficult than might be supposed. There is probably only one sequel to such a duel. The caterpillar may hurl itself into cover but the wasp will persist until it has been hunted down. Instinct guides the wasp in selecting the exact spot where her sting will paralyse it. Fabre gives a very interesting account of this which he likened to a surgical operation.

So from first to last it is a very strenuous life which these wasps live. The moment that the burrow is securely covered in, which may be three days after it was commenced, all memories of location, etc. are wiped out and the wasp begins to build up fresh images.

The pebble habit seems to have been adopted by individuals and cannot be regarded as a specific habit although it has been observed only in one species. How an individual can have started the habit is curious, but individuals of that same species have been observed using this tool while others continue to use only their own mandibles and the horny upper lip.

It is only wasps of this one species which are seen to use a tool to smooth their burrows, and only individuals among them. Times out of number the burrow is made in normal fashion and then one individual will be noticed pounding down earth with a stone.

We know that variations must occur in behaviour as well as in bodily form and so it is from individuals which carry out instinctive work a little differently from their fellows that we learn what amount of variation is possible in that race.

If we were to accept as a fact that insects can only act mechanically then there are instances of behaviour unexplained. There does indeed appear to be among insects a kind of elementary consciousness which is best described as awareness. In the case just quoted the wasp was aware that a hard stone would smooth the soil over her new burrow. The potter wasp which drove away flies because her nest had been tampered with was aware of interference, and it was this awareness not a mechanical impulse which induced a spontaneous action.

The potter wasp which moistened clay at a dripping tap was aware that it would serve her purpose as well as pond water, though other wasps were not making use of it. The leaf-cutting bee which carried a ball of pollen must have been influenced by some sort of awareness—perhaps of abnormal plenty—to make her adopt a new method of transporting pollen.

There are hundreds of examples that could be quoted where insects have been actuated by awareness of failure or awareness of danger to break away from hereditary instinct. Consciousness we must deny them, there is no evidence of the most highly developed insects performing purposeful actions. But when we consider the stage which has been reached in the evolution of instinctive behaviour we long for a glimpse into the future to learn to what heights their racial ideals may yet lead them.

# Index

Aerial tubers, ants' shelters in, 104-105

Airborne insects, 67-74

Amazon ants, 118-119

Ant lions, larvæ of, 14-15

Antennæ of mosquitoes, 24-29

Ants, army, invasion by, 135-141; camouflage of, 177-178; in competition for food, 192-198; cuckoo queens, 198-201; doping of, by predators, 124; food hunts by, 205-206; formic-acid defence of, 193-198; leaf homes of, 201-205; memory of, 188-189; olfactory sense of, 169; repulsed by bees, 155-156; shelter in trees and plants, 101-105; slavery among, 113, 116-119; social organization of, 153-155, 165-171

Aphid swarms, 72

Aquatic insects, 15-19; parasites of, 115; water-divining sense of, 32-34

Army ants, invasion by, 135-141

Army worms, invasion by, 141-144

Arum lilies, pollination of, 94-95

*Asclepiadaceæ*, pollination of, 95-98

Bates, Henry W., 43

Bees, chemotropic, 183-184; colour perception of, 32, 38; heliotropic, 182; individual actions of, 229-230; intoxication of, 124-125; memory of, 189-190; olfactory organs of, 31-32; parasites of, 42-43; pollination of orchids by, 84-88; social organization of, 155-156

Beetles, aquatic, 33-34; camouflage methods of, 176-177; carrion, 32; location of felled trees by, 39-40; mimicry of and among, 46-47; parasites of, 113-114; potato, 37; preparations for brood, 149-150; transportation of larvæ in logs, 77-78; whirligig, 34

Belt, Thomas, 43

Blossom beetle, 191-192

Blow-fly, 19-20

Body segments, independence of, 7-8

Breathing apparatus, 6-7

Bull's Horn Thorn, ants' shelters in, 103-104

Butterflies, 23; bodily characteristics of, 2; colour peception of, 37-38; migration of, 64-66; mimicry of, 45-46; Monarch, 44-45; olfactory sense of, 30-31; visual sense of, 35

Caddisworms, parasites of, 115

Camouflage methods, 176-178; *see also* Mimicry

Campanula as shelter, 80

Carrion beetles, 32

# Index

# Index

# Index